JUST
ANNIKA

JUST ANNIKA

with

Vivien Saunders

ABBOTSLEY PUBLISHING

Other books by Vivien Saunders:

The Complete Woman Golfer
The Young Golfer (with Clive Clarke)
The Golfing Mind
The Complete Book of Golf Practice
Golf for Women
Successful Golf
Advanced Golf
The Golf Handbook
The Women's Golf Handbook
Golf – The First 1000 Years

Published in 2013 by Abbotsley Publishing

Abbotsley Ltd
Eynesbury Hardwicke
St Neots
Cambridgeshire PE19 6XN

www.abbotsley.com

10 9 8 7 6 5 4 3 2 1

www.viviensaunders.com

A CIP catalogue record of this book is available from the British Library.

ISBN: 978-1-909730-03-8

Photo credits: Geraldine Giraux, Cathy McLeod, Jasmine Rahimi,
Keith Varney and Joy Williams
Edited by Marion Paull
Cover designed by Eric Drewery
Book designed by Bob Vickers

Printed and bound by Dolman Scott

Contents

Acknowledgements

This book was written by Welsh Cardigan corgi, Annika, with a little help from her owner, Vivien Saunders.

Vivien Saunders is a former British Women's Open Golf Champion, and the owner of the Abbotsley Golf Hotel and Country Club in Cambridgeshire. She is also a qualified solicitor but prefers to keep that a secret. She has written eleven books in her own name and ghost written books for three very special celebrities – Nick Faldo, Bernhard Langer, and now Annika, the Welsh Cardigan corgi. When Vivien was awarded the OBE, her friends assumed it was for her prowess as a domestic goddess; her wider audience knows it was for her services to golf!

We must first apologise to Pembroke corgis everywhere. But we still say the Queen made a mistake choosing you and not the Cardigans!

Secondly, we apologise for taking the name of Ingrid Grayling in vain. There probably is no finer dog whisperer in the business. In truth, she is adored by her doggy clients, and by most of their owners as well!

And thirdly, we thank Annika Sorenstam, who really is the best woman golfer the world has ever seen. She really did go round a golf course in 59 and is an inspiration to women golfers and Annikas everywhere. If our Annika had been called Bronwyn, this book would probably never have been written!

1
Welcome

Welcome to my diary. My name is Annika and I am a Welsh Cardigan corgi.

We are one of the most unusual breeds of British dogs. In the year I was born, just 68 new Welsh Cardigan corgi puppies were registered with the Kennel Club, where records of all the pedigree dogs born each year are kept. Actually, according to my owner, they keep records of *nearly* all pedigree dogs. I expect some owners fail to fill in the forms.

What do I look like!

I have a golden-retriever friend called Barney. You'll read plenty more about him in my diary. Retrievers are one of the most popular breeds of British dogs – 40,000 golden retrievers and Labradors (their close cousins) were registered in the year I was born, one of just 68. So we Cardigan corgis are very rare and very special.

I started this diary when I was about four months old. My life until then was very happy and content. I lived near Birmingham with my mum, Maggie, and her owner, Mrs Cole.

My mum has a really posh name – Yardican Diamond Drop, but everyone calls her Maggie. She's a champion and so has the initials CH in front of her name. I will never be a champion. Mum told me that when I was little.

My mum – Maggie

'Annika,' she said, 'there's far more to being a Cardigan corgi than being a show dog. I'm a champion because I have the cutest ears, the nicest fur, the longest body and all sorts of other special looks that people love. You, dear Annika, are going to do plenty of other things. Your legs are longer than mine and probably too long for you to be a champion, but you'll be able to herd sheep and cattle and play football, and do lots of other things a show champion can't do.'

My mum was born in Finland. I looked at Finland on a map and it's an awful long way away across the sea – much farther than from Birmingham to London. I never asked her how she got from Finland to England but I think it was in an aeroplane. Perhaps I'll go in a plane one day.

Mum had a litter of six puppies a few years before I was born. They had a different dad, so I suppose they are half brothers and sisters. Most of them are in Finland or Sweden and I've never met any of them.

I was one of a litter of six, too. My dad is Mandylay's Ultimately Blue. Mum and I are both black and white with brindle bits. Dad's a blue merle. He's smashing, so handsome and a Finnish champion. My brother Toby – Yardican King of Diamonds – is grand and I was so sad when he went to a new home. Kiki, Kween of Diamonds, went back to Finland and is a real champion. That's why she was called Kween of Diamonds because everyone knew she would be a glamour girl. And then there's Emily, Yardican Kwik Step. Mum says she was called Kwik Step because she can dance beautifully. I do see her sometimes. She isn't much fun. Two more brothers,

3

My daddy – Poco

Bryn and Totti, are blue merles like our dad. Bryn went to Wales to work on a farm and Totti went to Finland.

When we were all eight weeks old, people started coming to collect the others. First Toby went and then Kiki and Totti, Emily and finally Bryn. Mum seemed sad and I felt very lonely. Where had they all gone? Days went by, then a week, and no one came for me. Mum said it was because I was so special that Mrs Cole wouldn't sell me. I kept asking Mum if it meant I was going to be a show dog but she said it didn't. I began to feel quite sad. No one wanted to come for me. No, that's not really true. Sometimes I felt very sad that no one would come for me in a big car. Other times I thought I was the luckiest to be able to stay with Mum.

Mum taught me lots of things that the others probably didn't know. She told me that a really good trick when someone talks to you is to put your head on one side. People like to see dogs doing that. 'Remember, Annika, if you do ever go to a show, look the judge straight in the eye and just tip your head on one side when the judge speaks to you.'

Mum also taught me to walk backwards, which is quite a skill for a dog, and a few tricks of the trade for getting biscuits. 'If two people are in the house, they might be confused about whether you've had your supper. Always look as if you're expecting a meal. Nudging your bowl with your nose can be convincing.'

Mum taught me all the tricks for training humans.

'They think they train us, but we train them. They don't know how to make us do what they want, so they go to classes and read books, and watch programmes on television. All we do, Annika, is pass on the skills from one generation to another. That's why it's good for a little dog like you to stay with your mother for so long. I worry whether Toby and Kiki got all the messages from me in those first two months before they went, but you, Annika, you will learn everything I can tell you.

'I think Mrs Cole may be keeping you so that one day you'll have puppies of your own. I'll teach you how that works in due course. You're called Yardican Kween Bee. That's because people talk about having babies as learning about the birds and the bees. Remember, Annika, it takes nine weeks for a new mum to have her puppies. When you're a little older, I'll explain how mummies and daddies have pups.'

'Tell me now, Mum.'

'No Annika, there's plenty of time for that. First we must concentrate on keeping your fur and feet clean, what to eat and what you must never eat, and lots of day-to-day things all corgis need to know.'

I was born in late October. That's a good time for puppies to be born because we're ready to go to a new home at Christmas. But sometimes people give a puppy as a Christmas present and the puppies aren't really wanted. I saw a car with a sticker in the window saying: 'A Dog is for Life, not just for Christmas'. It made me cry to think of it.

By Christmas, all my brothers and sisters had left home, so it was just Mum and me. My first Christmas was great. There was so much food in the house and Mrs Cole had all her family round to visit. The smells from the kitchen were wonderful. I was really hoping we'd get a special supper, but Mum, as always, was full of good advice.

'Never eat turkey. It will give you a rash on your nose and make you poorly. As for chocolates – dog chocolates and people chocolates are very different, and eating a people chocolate can be fatal for dogs. You could die. I think chocolates are so dangerous to eat that people give them to other people they don't really like at Christmas. The man over the road called his wife's mother a bitch and gave her a box of chocolates. But she survived OK. Anyway, Annika, never eat turkey or chocolates at Christmas.'

Me as a puppy

And then in March, when I was about four and a half months old, I heard Mrs Cole on the phone, talking about me.

'Her name is Annika. Yes, she'll be a great pet. Will you let her have puppies? Yes, we'll see you in two hours. I've a bed for Annika and I'll send her with some food.'

'Oh, Mum. Do you think someone's coming to fetch me? What will they be like? How will you know where to contact me? Where will I go? Oh, help, help, Mum. When will I see you again?'

It was a terrible time, waiting for the car to arrive. I heard Mrs Cole on the phone again.

'Yes, Annika's going. I'm sure she'll have a very good home. She's going to live on a golf course, near Cambridge.'

'Mum, the car's coming. Help! Don't let them take me. What's a golf course? Oh, please come too!'

I was so frightened. Would I see Mum again?

And then the car came. It was large and green. The driver and her friend climbed out and met Mrs Cole. They exchanged typical people comments.

'Yes, she's called Annika. Why did you laugh at her name?'

The new owner explained that she played golf and that I would be living on a golf course and playing golf, and that Annika is the most famous woman golfer in the whole world and is Swedish. 'Oh, my God, Mum. I'm going to be famous.'

The owner paid lots of money for me. I wasn't being given away because no one wanted me. The car I was going in was larger than the one that collected Toby or Bryn or Emily. I would be all right. I kissed Mum long and hard and she quickly reminded me of some of the little tricks to make them love and want me.

'Remember, Annika. Walk close beside your owner, come back when called, don't mix with cats and just tilt your head to the side so they think you understand. Good luck, sweetest of my young ones. Goodbye Annika.'

The new owner – whom I thought would be a pushover, but turned into Miss Bossy Boots – popped me into a large white crate for safe travelling in the back of the car. 'Do you think she'll be all right in there?' I heard her say to her friend. 'It's better than on your lap or the back seat.'

When Toby went he sat up by the window of the car and we waved and woofed. Emily sat on her new owner's lap and Mum and I could see her go. But I couldn't see anything. I just woofed to Mum. 'See you sometime, Mum.'

2

I Discover Cats

We seemed to travel for ages. I'd only ever been in a car to go to the vet's for injections and check-ups. Eventually, the car stopped and the new owner got out. She opened the rear door, lifted me out of my crate and all my fears disappeared. In front of me was a big, big house surrounded by a garden with trees and flower beds, and water. If only I could let Mum know that I would be all right here. I heard the new owner on the phone to Mrs Cole. 'Yes, we've arrived

I love my new home

home safely and Annika travelled fine. I'll keep in touch and let you know how she is.'

Well, the new house seemed great. Lots to sniff. Plenty to see.

And water. Oh my goodness. I crept slowly down the bank to see the water. What would Mum say? She would tell me to be careful. She would tell me to slide on my belly and look out for things to hang on to. In the water, fish swam up and down, up and down – stupid things – and a brown duck paddled along, leading her babies. Mother duck didn't like me. 'Go away, go away.' At least, I got the idea that's what she said. I don't speak duck, so I thought it best to do what Mum had told me to do and tilt my head to one side to pretend I understood. Off swam the duck and her babies. They didn't look very interesting anyway.

'Oh my goodness me. What's that?'

In the water I could see another one of me. As I moved, the other me moved from side to side, too. It was copying me – scary. I tapped the surface with my paw and the other me moved with the ripples. The other corgi wasn't there at all. It was a picture of me, floating in the water. Fish, ducks, moving images – what fun!

But then things took a turn for the worse. As I looked in the water, watching myself, I also saw, something else, moving very, very slowly. It definitely wasn't a corgi. I could feel it creeping up behind me and I could see its reflection in the water.

'Help, Mum, I want to come home.'

The creature was huge, golden and white, with big, scary, staring eyes. Its tail stood tall and had a tiny curl at the top, and its ears were so pointed. I was terrified. I turned towards it. Mum had always warned me about cats but I had never seen a real one, just on the television. This one was more frightening than I could have imagined.

He spoke to me in his best cat talk. I didn't need to understand it perfectly. It was obvious what he meant. 'Go away. This is my patch. I am Edward. You can call me Sir Edward. [I did understand that.] I have the run of the house and you will stay in the kitchen.'

Mum warned me never to tangle with cats

Edward stares and is very frightening

I remembered what Mum had told me. Only look fierce if you're going to win. A cat will outstare any dog, even a border collie. I wished Mum was here to help. I thought it best to let Edward know I accepted he was the boss (for now at any rate), so I lay down and rolled on my back. But I was thinking, 'Wait until I grow much bigger than you, Sir Edward.'

'Annika, Annika,' shouted my owner, but I was too frightened of Edward to move towards the house. 'Oh, you've met Edward,' she said, coming down the garden to find me. 'Now come on you two. Time for tea.'

We both sauntered towards the kitchen door. I thought it was polite to let him through first. I had always let Mum through a door in front of me. She said it was just good manners. I stood aside for Edward. In his politest cat talk he spat out, 'Ladies first.'

'What a kind cat, after all,' I thought. But as I trotted inside he whacked me on the bottom. It stung. Mum had warned me about cats' claws. I remember we watched a lovely TV programme about the Cheshire Cat, a cat that smiled and grinned. Edward was just like that.

'Come on, Annika. Don't be shy of Edward. He's a lovely boy,' said our owner.

I knew from then on that Edward was in charge. He always has been. He had his bowl of biscuits in one corner of the kitchen and I had mine in the other corner. But there was another little bowl with more biscuits. Who were these for? I decided that if they weren't eaten by Edward, they must be for me, or perhaps we had another visitor.

After tea our owner put all the bowls on the worktop. Who was the other bowl for?

I spent my first evening looking round the house and garden. Edward just stared at me. Everywhere I went Edward watched. He smiled at me and spat. He seemed to laugh. He had his own little door and could come and go as he wanted. 'That's a cat flap,' he informed me. 'It's not for dogs. You'll get stuck.' I popped my head through. Frightening, frightening. Edward was there.

'Come on, Annika, you need to go out before bedtime. Wee wee. Be a good girl.'

It was dark, terribly dark. Edward laughed. Cats can see in the dark but I wasn't so sure. I ran to the end of the garden to the bank above the water. Floodlights came on in the garden behind me. There, I could see just like Edward could.

'Oh, my goodness, gracious me. What's that? I think it's a dragon. I watched a TV programme about dragons with Mum.' Staring out from the other side of the water was a huge, black figure with enormous ears. It moved from side to side, mocking me and taunting me. At least the dragon couldn't get to me. I barked at it. It didn't bark back. I charged to the right and it followed me. I crept to the left. It followed me. It was terrifying. I so wished that Mum was with me. Brother Toby would have known what to do.

And then the lights in the garden went off and I couldn't see the dragon. Where had he gone? Edward was just sitting by the back door, mocking me, laughing like cats do.

'Fine guard dog you're going to be. Scared of your own shadow.'

The farmer over the road from Mum's house had a collie dog called Shadow and I certainly wasn't afraid of him. Silly Edward. But I was afraid of the dragon.

'Have you been a good girl, Annika? Now, as a treat you're going to sleep upstairs. Just until we get you a nice bed in the kitchen.'

I was going upstairs. Mrs Cole had stairs in her house but neither Mum nor I had been allowed to go up them. Toby once went upstairs and Mrs Cole's husband shouted at him so loudly that he never did it again. 'Playing on the stairs can kill. Slips and trips.'

Now I was going to have to go upstairs. My owner just walked up ahead of me, leaving me sitting at the bottom. I

Edward loves his little, warm bed

watched her do it so easily. One foot and then the other. 'Come on, Annika, up you come.'

I froze and shook at the bottom, one paw on the bottom step. How did she do it? It looks easy with two feet but how do you fit on to stairs with four feet? Please come down and show me again. Slips and trips. Accidents on the stairs can kill.

My luck was in. The owner came downstairs again. 'I'd better take you a bowl of water for the night.'

I sat and watched. Up she went again. One by one. How would I do it? Remember, stairs are dangerous. Slips and trips. I put my front paws on the first stair. Where would my back paws go? I swung them out to the side on the bottom stair. All four paws on the stair. That didn't seem right. How do I do it? I wish Mum and Toby were here to show me. Front paws on to the next stair. Back paws on to the stair. That can't be right. Think Annika. And then along came the wretched Edward.

'Watch me you silly dog. Go two at a time. Just like this.'

Up he leapt. I put my front paws up two steps, back paws on to the stairs below. Front paws up again, back paws up again. Mum and Toby would be so proud of me. And then I looked to the side. Through the railings I could see the floor a long way down. I kept on going.

'Come on, Annika. Here's where you sleep. Dogs aren't allowed on beds in this house but just this once. As it's your first night.'

The owner lifted me on to her bed. Wow, this was very different from the kennel I shared with Mum. I wondered what she would be doing without me. I expect she missed me. I certainly missed her but I had plenty to think about as I settled down to sleep. So much had happened that day. I had woken up not knowing I was to leave Mum. I had travelled in a huge car in a crate, talked to ducks, met my first cat and been frightened by the large, black dragon. Despite all that, I thought I was going to like it here.

The owner gave me a cuddle. 'Goodnight, Annika.' I remembered to tip my head to the side so she knew I understood. A low, rumbling noise came from the corner of the room. There he was, Sir Edward, curled up in his own grey bed, hanging on the radiator, purring and snoring. I think Edward and I will be friends one day.

Goodnight Owner. Goodnight Edward. Goodnight Mum. I'm thinking of you. Sweet dreams.

3

My New Home

I had a good first night. Edward purred and the owner purred. Her purring was louder. It sounded like the motorbike belonging to Mrs Cole's son. Vroom, vroom.

'Good morning, Annika,' said the owner. Edward was nowhere to be seen but he made his presence felt just the same. 'Oh no, Edward's brought us a present.'

Sure enough, there on the carpet beside the bed was a little grey mouse. It was very still. I thought it might be nice to play with, so I jumped off the bed. The mouse shot under it and the owner screamed. I squirmed under the bed and there, with his paw firmly on the mouse, was Edward. He stared at me with big green eyes and the mouse stared at me with little black eyes. And I remembered how collies on the farm behaved in controlling sheep. I plucked up courage and stared at Edward. He stared; I stared. He stared some more and I stared back. The owner kept on screaming.

What would Mum do? I woofed, just a very little woof but it surprised Edward. He took his paw off the mouse and it ran off under the wardrobe.

Edward and I both crawled out from under the bed and the owner stopped screaming. Then she bent over and looked under the bed. Where was the mouse? She screamed some more and retreated on to the bed. 'Where is that mouse?'

That experience taught me the order of superiority in the house. The mouse must be the boss, Edward next in command and me third. I assumed the owner was screaming because she thought Edward had killed the mouse, and then she couldn't find the mouse. He must be very important.

'Come on, you two, breakfast.' I stood at the top of the stairs and realised I didn't know how to get down. Going up was fine; Edward had shown me that. But going down looked frightening. The owner stood beside me. I looked up at her, as lovingly as possible. She picked me up. What a dream! She carried me down.

Get me down these stairs, please

Edward and I had a good breakfast, with Edward on the worktop and me on the floor. I soon learnt that cats eat very differently from dogs and will pick at their food during the day and night. I was used to eating mine quickly, essential when all six puppies and Mum were being fed at the same time. Toby would scoff the food if we didn't. I thought it best to keep eating quickly, just in case Edward stole my food. But he never did.

'Now Annika, you're going to have your first introduction to golf. If you can make a really good golfing dog, you can go to loads of exciting places and have great days out.'

She didn't know I knew about the world famous Annika the golfer. I was going to emulate her and be famous in my own right.

'OK, Annika, this is a golf ball. Under no circumstances must you ever, ever touch a golf ball.'

I couldn't understand why. I remembered never to touch turkey at Christmas or people chocolates or toads. Mum had warned me about toads, which could kill. And grapes. I remember her telling Emily about the danger of grapes. They could fall on the kitchen floor and were fun to chase but were very, very dangerous for dogs to eat. But never had she spoken of golf balls.

I lay down and the owner put a golf ball right by my nose. It smelt interesting. I had never smelt anything like this before. I so wanted to touch it. It didn't look dangerous. The owner walked away and I just nudged the golf ball. It ran away, rather like the mouse, but just a few inches. I lay there so still when

I mustn't touch the golf ball

the owner returned. I hoped she might think the golf ball had moved on its own but she knew. She put the golf ball back by my nose.

'Annika, I told you not to touch the golf ball. No.'

I looked up at her with the cutest eyes I could, but I felt a little ashamed.

'Right, Annika, that's your first golf lesson. Now we're off to meet some friends and do some shopping for your bed and bowls.'

After a short car ride we arrived at the golf club and the owner took me in. Several people were there to greet us. People look very, very tall to little dogs. I liked the people who crouched down to see me. It's nice to talk to them at eye level and far friendlier.

They all seemed thrilled to meet me. 'Isn't she sweet?' 'What's her name?' 'Annika – she's called Annika?' 'Oh, how funny. Annika, of course.'

My owner explained that Mrs Cole had never heard of world famous golfer, Annika Sorenstam, and had chosen it because Annika is just a really nice Scandinavian name and Mum and Dad are both from Finland. I learnt to love my special name and it has made me famous as a golfing dog.

'What is she?' 'Has she got some corgi in her?' 'What sort of cross is she? Is she half collie and half dachshund?'

My owner explained, as she has explained, many, many times since, that I am a Welsh Cardigan corgi. She tells them that there are two types of corgis – the Pembroke and the Cardigan. The Cardigans are larger than the Pembrokes. They have huge ears, slightly turned-out feet and have always had their tails. I couldn't understand about the tails. Of course we have tails. She told them how Cardigan corgis are possibly the oldest breed of British dog and were used, and still are, for herding cattle. Cardigans will walk anything up to fourteen miles behind a herd of cattle, snapping at the cattle's heels to drive them on. Some farmers use us with sheep, but we are generally considered too strong for sheep.

'So,' I thought, 'my role is to drive cattle. But where and when will I get the chance?'

Everyone fussed over me and spoke to me. I just put my head to the side to let them know I understood, or to pretend I understood.

On the way back, we visited the pet shop. What a grand

experience! All sorts of lovely biscuits and food goodies were available just at nose height. I chose a couple of chew sticks and walked around with them. And then I spied it. I dropped the chews. Who would want chews when the real jewel was there? It was like the forbidden golf ball but larger and red. People think dogs are colour blind but that's not true for all of us. I woofed at it; and woofed again. I looked up at it. The owner pulled it off the rack and it squeaked. Oh goodness, it squeaked. It talked to me in dog talk. 'Buy me,' it said. It's a talking ball. Can I have it? Please let me have it. I must have it. Yes, she's buying it for me. And she picked up the chews. Oh forget them. It's the ball I want.

And then we chose a bed, a lovely red and blue bed with a soft, furry cushion; and a new collar with a matching lead. I'm going to be so smart. But the ball. The talking ball. Yippee! We never had balls to play with at home with Mum, but she told me about them. She knew other dogs who had them and loved them.

The owner put me in the back of the car, in my own compartment. She took out the paper bag from the pet shop. Yes, yes, yes, I'm going to get the talking ball. But no, she gave me one of the two chews and a biscuit and filled my special bowl with water. But no ball.

We arrived home and she unloaded me and the shopping. 'Come on, Annika. Be a good girl. Wee wee.'

I didn't want a wee wee. I wanted the ball. But I knew to pretend to wee on the grass to make her happy. People get obsessed by seeing a dog wee. People are weird like that. We don't watch them. But she was happy and in we went. She unwrapped the new bed and my blanket and lead and collar and a little badge with my name and phone number. And then I had a few biscuits and some milk but still no ball. Eventually, she unwrapped it and left it on the worktop. I looked at it and woofed to call it down to me but it wouldn't come. Silly ball. Come here. But it wouldn't.

The owner spoke to me about the bed and where I would sleep. It seems I was to sleep down in the kitchen and not upstairs. Edward sauntered into the kitchen, tail flicking. He strutted across to me. 'There, dog, you're going to sleep downstairs. Cats sleep upstairs. A dog's place is in the kitchen.'

With that he jumped up on to the worktop to his bowl of little biscuits. Edward is so arrogant. And then, joy of joys, he

He gets everywhere!

tapped at the little, red, talking ball and it spun on to the floor. It bounced right down at my feet. Edward thought it would frighten me; that's why he did it. But I had waited and waited. I picked up the ball and ran out into the back garden.

'Come here, Annika.' Not a chance. I just ran with the ball and tossed it into the air. It spun and bounced and squeaked to talk to me. The talking ball was alive. I didn't want the owner to have it in case she took it away and put it on the worktop. I ran and ran with it. It squeaked and laughed. What a good friend.

'Come here, Annika.' No, I will not. You'll take it away. I dropped the talking ball and shouted at it. It didn't shout back. It only squeaked when I carried it. I sat looking at the ball and then, huge horrors, the owner grabbed the ball from right under my nose. 'Woof, woof. Give me that ball. I'll woof and woof until you give it back.' The owner had a mean, mean streak and threw the ball away, but I saw where it went and collected it. She wouldn't get it from me again.

'Give me the ball, Annika.' I refused. I ran off and the owner chased me. Eventually, she got to me and did something really cruel. She asked me for the ball and then offered me a biscuit. I was hungry after all this exercise and couldn't resist the biscuit. Could I be quick enough to snatch the biscuit but keep the ball? No, I could not. I took the biscuit but lost the ball. She had it again. She threw it away again. I fetched it and ran off with it. The owner called me and offered me another biscuit. Ball or biscuit? Biscuit of course. And then she threw the ball. She was trained – it was as easy as that. I bring you the ball and you give me a biscuit.

Happiness is a lovely red ball

Our ball playing developed over the next days and weeks. I soon found that the talking ball would fly into the air and land with a squeak, and I could catch it. Catching it became far more fun than the biscuit. Soon the owner was trained in the routine. She would throw the ball, I would bring it back and she would throw it, over and over again. Edward used to sit and watch but he could never beat me with the ball.

That second night I slept in my own bed in the kitchen. I was quite frightened. On my last visit to the garden that night the lights had come on again and the large black dragon was tormenting me from the other side of the water. Again it followed me along the other side of the bank. It was huge and very, very scary. So when I curled up in my bed, I just hoped the owner had locked the back door to keep the dragon out. I dreamt of the little white forbidden golf ball and of the bigger red talking ball, and of all those people greeting me and wondering what I was. A Welsh Cardigan corgi. That's me. One of Britain's oldest breeds of dog – and with a very special name. Goodnight Mum, and love to Toby and Emily and Bryn; and Kiki and Totti in Finland. And love to you, Edward, for knocking the talking ball on to the floor for me. I wonder what tomorrow holds in store.

Goodnight Totti in Finland

4

Born to Play Games

Life with my new owner was fun, and I continued to train her to play with me, especially with my squeaky, talking ball, which I loved. Then one morning we had a disaster. The squeaky ball ran off into the water, and as loudly as I shouted to it, it refused to come back. My owner came to see why I was woofing.

'Oh, you silly girl. Fetch it.'

I crept down to the water's edge somewhat fearfully, because it was near where I saw the dragon each night. 'You can do it,' I said to myself, and cautiously ventured a paw in the water. It was cold. I stepped in a bit farther and got close to the ball. 'Woof, come to me.' I stuck my nose forward and it shot farther away. I opened my mouth and tried to grab it. The ball swam off towards the dragon's den on the other side of the water. 'Come back. The dragon will get you tonight.'

And then my owner came to help me. She brought a long rake, grabbed the ball and pulled it towards us. Slowly, slowly the ball swam back towards me, but just as it reached the bank I closed my mouth on to it and it shot off again. My owner climbed down the bank, pulled the ball back again and scooped it up with the rake, flinging it back on to the lawn. It was saved and I ran over to it. What fun it had been to watch

Please throw it for me

the owner collect the ball with the rake. She was still down at the bottom of the bank, so I pushed the ball with my nose and it rolled down the bank into the water again. I woofed and shouted with glee. The owner scooped it up again with the rake and threw it back on to the lawn. Just as she clambered up the bank, the naughty, squeaking ball ran off down the bank again.

'Annika. What are you doing?'

Not me. Would I do that? Would I push the ball back? The owner collected the ball again and put it in her pocket. The game was over. As she walked along, the ball kept squeaking and talking to me. 'Get me out of here,' squeaked the ball. But the owner had the ball and I didn't. We returned to the kitchen and she put the talking ball on to the worktop – Edward's worktop. That was the end of the game. It was a sad moment. Edward sauntered in and leapt up on to the worktop. He teased me by stepping very gently round the talking ball; the ball just sat there. I woofed to Edward to knock it down for me but he wasn't having any of it. Bother him.

Then, joy of joys, a visitor arrived for tea. 'I've come to see Annika. Is this her? Isn't she lovely. What huge ears. What is she? Has she some corgi in her? She looks like a collie … oh, she's a Cardigan corgi. I didn't know there were such things. The Queen has corgis doesn't she?!'

The Queen has corgis. Did my ears deceive me? The Queen. The actual Queen has corgis. We are famous. And then I spotted something. The visitor had brought a little bag, which had my name on it. 'For Annika'. She sat it on the kitchen table with her handbag. The owner gave her a cup of tea and they chatted on as people do, about this and that. And that and this. On and on. And then she started looking at me again.

'I've brought a few goodies for Annika,' she said. 'A couple of chewy biscuits and a packet of special treats. And I've also brought her a ball but I see she's already got one, so I suppose she won't want this one.'

She was all ready to put the ball back in her bag but I remembered what Mum had taught me. I cocked my head on one side, looked her straight in the eye and gave a tiny, very polite woof.

'Do you think she would like the ball? Is she allowed another one?'

Why won't you squeak to me!

He is just too close for comfort

'Woof,' I replied before my owner could get a word in first. 'Here you are, Annika.'

I grabbed the ball and shot out of the kitchen door with it. Freedom. This ball didn't talk. I bit it gently and pushed it but it wouldn't talk. I urged the owner to come and play, but she and the visitor were still drinking tea. So I pushed the ball along with my nose and then tossed it into the air. If the owner wouldn't play, I would have to play ball on my own. I pushed it along with my nose and then with my toes. Quickly, quickly, this way and that. The ball danced along on its own. I ran the length of the lawn with it – a nudge with my nose, a nudge with my toes. And then, horrors, it ran towards the water. 'Stop, stop. Please stop.' Edward sat in a flower bed and laughed at me. The wicked ball ran off down the bank and into the water. My game was over.

'Go and get the ball you silly dog,' spat Edward.

'Will you help me?' I shouted but he refused.

'I've told you before, cats don't like water.'

'And that's why dogs don't like cats,' I whispered to myself.

So down I clambered, slowly, steadily, slithering on my belly until the ball was just below me. I nudged it with my nose and it moved farther away into the water. Edward laughed. Horrid cat! I nudged it again and away it went. There was nothing for it. I crept out slowly into the water. My toes sank into the mud, but I was not going to let the ball get away. 'Come here.' But this ball didn't talk like the other one. I crept out farther into the water, right up to my tummy, but I could still feel the bottom. Carefully, carefully I stepped out into the

Learning to swim

water and there was the ball just in front of me. 'Come here,' I woofed again, but it didn't respond. I shouted at the ball, but it was stubborn. It refused to listen and just swam a couple of inches farther away. I crept just a tiny bit farther and could feel my body and feet lift off. I was floating. I didn't like it. I was so close to where the dragon came out at night but it had to be done. I reached the naughty ball and grabbed it with my teeth. Once more it shot away. 'Be gentle,' I thought, and I just hugged the ball steadily with my teeth. I carried it back to the bank and up on to the lawn. The ball was rescued. I nudged it back towards the house, a nudge with my nose and a tap with my toes.

'Annika, what are you doing? Look how clever she is. She's going to be a real footballer is our Annika.'

I still wanted the talking ball but that was out of reach on Edward's worktop. Please leave me with this ball. I nudged it under the kitchen table and there it stayed.

*

Food was kept in the pantry, a little room with lots of shelves. All manner of tins and packets were there for the owner, and packets of biscuits and tins for Edward. Then there was my food – a large drum of biscuits, plus my chews and other goodies.

By now it was springtime and the owner changed my meal times from three to two, just like Edward's. One night we had a change.

'Would you all like sardines? That's a treat.'

She opened a little oblong tin with a lid that pulled off. I could smell them straight away. The owner put some sardines and oil in my dish, some in Edward's dish and some in a third dish. I had seen that third little dish before. I wondered who that was for. Then Edward did something very strange. He jumped off the worktop and waited on the floor beside me. He sat up on his bottom and put up both front paws.

'There's a clever boy. Begging for the sardines.'

'What are you doing, Edward?'

'It's called begging. If you were a real dog, you'd know about begging. It's what we do to show we want something. People can't resist us. Learn to do that and you can get anything you want – within reason. Why don't you know about begging?'

I suppose Mum had never taught me. Mum was so long in the body that I couldn't really imagine her begging. It would take lots of balance, but I was prepared to give it a go. I sat back on my bottom, like Edward did, front paws up, and teetered backwards and forwards. He was better at it than I was.

'There you are, kids, sardines for a special occasion.' Down went my bowl and down went Edward's bowl and the owner put the third one up on the worktop.

I gobbled my food, just like in the old days when Toby would eat his so quickly and try to grab mine, but Edward seemed to eat in slow motion, savouring the fish. The sardines were lovely, oily and smelly and not at all like biscuits. The temptation to take some of his was too strong and I slid over towards him, but he turned and spat at me.

'Don't you get any funny ideas about pinching my food, Dog.'

I remembered what Mum had said about not trusting cats but I couldn't resist the pull of the sardines. I crept still closer to Edward and his bowl and he turned towards me. I thought for a moment that I could grab one and Edward would be too slow and sleepy to realise what was happening. I had observed him for several weeks now and he spent most of the time asleep. He would sleep every morning in the lounge on a chair. Then, in the afternoon, he would find a place in the garden and curl up under a bush; always the same one. And then in the evening, after tea, he would return to the lounge and curl up on a different chair. Finally, at night, I supposed he would go to sleep in the owner's bedroom in his little grey hammock on the radiator. Edward was a slow, lazy creature who, by my observations, had never moved at more than a slow, steady saunter. Mum used to call it snail's pace.

I had never seen him move other than slowly and sedately. I would take my chance with the sardine. I rushed forward and grabbed at it. Edward's right paw shot out faster than anything I had ever seen before – faster than the owner's car, faster than an aeroplane overhead, faster than the talking ball could ever move. And the paw had knives on the end, sharp, sharp claws, which caught me right on the side of my nose. I yelled and woofed and backed off very quickly. Mum was right. Never trust a cat. How could something so slow and lazy become so fast in a split second?

'Oh, Annika, you silly girl. Just leave Edward's food alone. We'll have to feed him on the worktop in future. Come on you two. Let's light a fire and watch the television.'

It was quite a warm day for having a fire but the flames in the wood burner flickered and the warmth was cosy and made me sleepy. The owner put a bottle of wine on the top of the wood burner to warm through and Edward and I sat either end of the sofa. The owner brought my bed into the lounge and put it near the fire. Oh, joy of joys. I slid off towards my bed but before I could get there Edward was in it – in my bed. He smiled that wicked smile that only a cat can give, his cool green eyes just flashing and his whiskers quivering. And then he opened his mouth and yawned, and yawned again. He curled up contentedly – he had taken over *my* bed. I really didn't dare to get in beside him. He looked sweet and docile and I was tempted, but I remembered that flash of speed with the sardines and reckoned it could happen any time.

I curled up on the sofa again and fell asleep in the warmth of the fire. I could hear Edward purring or snoring, I wasn't quite sure which, but he always seemed to sleep with one eye just opening slightly every now and then to keep watch on his surroundings. In my dreams I thought of the fun with the ball, of rescuing it from the water and then nudging and nosing it along.

I heard the owner on the phone to Mrs Cole. 'Annika is quite a girl. She and Edward are going to be the best of pals. He's even in her bed.'

Edward is in my bed; so I am in his!

'Yes,' I thought, 'and you won't catch me in there with him.'

When I had outgrown my puppy bed, it was supposed to be for Edward and I had a new, larger one. But, typically, Edward would sleep in my large bed and I would hang out of the little one, which by then was far too small. The owner bought me a little house-like bed, with a felt roof and soft cushions. When it arrived, I was so thrilled, but Edward got in it. Every time I tried to go in it, Edward would be there first. So the owner had to buy us one each. That evening started the trend.

The owner had put on the television to watch some sport. First there was swimming. I watched carefully and realised this was how to retrieve a ball from water. I could see the strokes. It looked quite easy and I was sure I could do it. Four legs would certainly be better than two, although I didn't like the look of the dive. But swimming was definitely for me.

And then I saw Edward's sport – boxing. None of the fighters had anything like the speed of Edward. They would thrust out their arms with amazing speed, but nothing like him. 'It's Muhammad Ali, the Greatest. He floats like a butterfly, stings like a bee,' shouted the commentator. But even Muhammad Ali was slow by comparison to Edward. The boxers wore gloves. I knew why this was. It was obviously to protect the other man from knifelike claws. That's what Edward needed. He needed gloves. I saw one boxer draw blood from his opponent, even with the gloves on. Think of the damage Edward could do. I looked over at him and he was fast asleep, but one eye was slightly open, looking at me. He looked like an angel, but an angel with vicious claws.

And then came golf. So this was the game I was destined to play. It looked slow and boring. A man hit a ball with a long stick, walked after it, hit it again with another stick and then finally hit it into a hole. The little white ball was just like the one the owner had presented to me with the warning never to touch. After the man had hit his ball into the hole, he took it out. He touched it, but that seemed OK. The owner had said I would learn to be a good golfing dog. I couldn't see any golfing dogs on the TV. Perhaps there was a different version for dogs. But it did involve a ball and a stick and fresh air and long walks. Obviously, this was the sport for me. Yes, Annika the golfing dog.

I nodded off again, with thoughts of ball games and

paddling in the water. And then, suddenly, the room was alive with the noise of shouting and excitement from the TV. I have to explain that dogs with huge, stand-up ears like mine have very superior hearing. Some say that Cardigan corgis have the best hearing of all dogs. The noise from the TV was a real disturbance to my ears.

Another game was in full swing. 'It's Beckham,' shouted the commentator, and I watched enthralled. Forget golf. This was the real thing – football. In that short fifteen minutes I realised that this was my game. This was what I wanted to do. I watched them dribble the ball with such skill and speed. They wouldn't let the ball go down into water. They would control it and make it swerve. They nudged it with their feet in straight lines and circles, and would push the ball past another player. And then one player kicked the ball into the air and another caught it on his chest, nudged it with his feet, tossed it with his head and butted it into the goal. I could do that.

The commentator shouted, 'Hasn't he got wonderful hand-eye co-ordination. It's Beckham in control again. Number 7 in red; look at that skill.'

That's me. Paw and nose co-ordination. A little nudge here and a little nudge there, a nose to the right of the ball and a paw to the left. Yes, yes, yes. Forget golf, think football.

And then, in front of me, were players in black and white. My colours. 'It's the Magpies.' They were from Newcastle. Where's Newcastle? Will we ever go there? Can I have a larger ball, not just a little squeaky, talking ball but one just large enough for football? Can I?

'Come on, Annika, out one last time before bed.' I rushed out, hoping to avoid the dragon. But the floodlights at the back of the house came on and as I ran to the back of the garden and the edge of the water, there was the black dragon, taunting me from the other bank. His huge ears mimicked mine. As I ran to the right, so did he. He followed me everywhere, and the louder I shouted and the faster I moved, so did he. Please leave me alone. Every night.

That night I slept downstairs in the kitchen. The owner had left the door open and I had the run of the house, but it was time for sleep and dreaming of swimming and football and golf (I suppose). In the middle of the night, a huge commotion broke out at the other end of the kitchen. Edward was shouting and meowing, making a noise I had never heard before. His back was up and his tail was huge. He looked so different.

And then I saw it. Another enormous cat, black and white and fluffy, and Edward was clearly terrified of it. I plucked up courage and rushed past Edward straight for the other cat. It shot off at huge speed and clattered through Edward's cat flap. I ran to the cat flap but couldn't get through. The big, black cat was staring back at me. It spat from the safety of outside.

Edward was wounded by the big cat. His ear was bleeding and his nose had a little scratch. He was limping towards me and squealing quite sadly.

'Annika, how can I thank you enough?'

'Who on earth was that?'

'He's called Spare Cat, at least that's what the owner calls him. He doesn't live here. He lives in the workmen's shed next door, or sometimes under the shed at the end of the garden. He's wild and aggressive and very frightening. He's what's called a feral cat, living off his wits. He catches mice and birds and terrorises the area. The owner managed to catch him once and Cat Rescue collected him but he came back. Last night he must have smelt our sardines and decided he wanted some. I've never been able to keep him away. The owner will have to take me to the vet in the morning. I think my leg's broken, my ear's been bitten and my nose feels sore. Annika, you were so brave to send away the Spare Cat. He could have killed me. He has a very bad temper.'

'Don't worry, Edward. I'll protect you from Spare Cat. He seemed quite frightened of me.'

'I told Spare Cat you were a wolf and he believed me. But, dear Annika, you probably did save my life.'

'Can we be friends now? My mum warned me about cats and how I must respect you, but it would be good if we could be real friends. I'll make you an honest promise. I'll always save you from Spare Cat and chase him away if you will save me from the nasty Black Dragon who taunts and frightens me every night. Edward, let's be pals.'

I thought I saw Edward wink. He cuddled up with me in my bed and we were destined to be friends. But I remembered Mum's words. Never trust a cat. Goodnight Mum. Goodnight Toby and Emily and Kiki, wherever you are. I'm going to be a footballer.

5

Edward's Story

The next day, just as Edward had predicted, our owner had to take him to the vet's. He had a torn ear and was still limping. She packed us both in the car. Edward sat in a little box and I sat on the back seat in a special blue harness, which kept me safe.

'Is that a Cardigan corgi?' said the receptionist, once we'd made it inside, Edward still in his box, me on my lead. 'I've never seen a Cardigan corgi. Isn't she great!' I felt puffed up with pleasure.

The vet put me on the weighing scales, looked at the chart and said I was just right for my age. But poor Edward, he had to have ointment and tablets, and the vet thought he was in a pretty bad way. The owner explained that the Spare Cat had been back again and had attacked Edward. The vet told Edward he was a brave boy.

On the way home, Edward and I had quite a conversation. It isn't always easy for cats and dogs to discuss things but we had an understanding. Edward warned me about cars and vans. Mum had told me that cars and vans can be dangerous but Edward explained more. He loved cars and had a habit of getting in them if the window was open. Vans were even better because they were often full of boys' toys, and tools

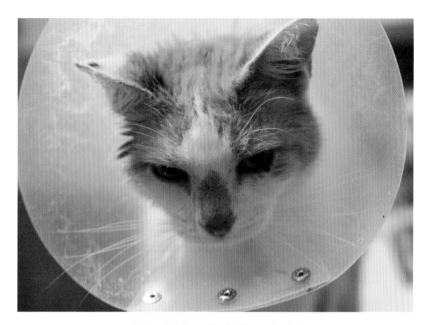

Injured Edward in his lampshade!

and blankets and rugs. Cats are known to be very inquisitive and Edward confessed that he was just like this. He couldn't remember much about his background but he remembered that he had been warned by his mother never to mess with cars.

Nevertheless, one day he had climbed into a van that had come to visit his home. He cuddled up in the back and the van drove off. It seemed to travel for many hours until it finally stopped outside the owner's house, and the driver got out. He opened the back doors to pick up a parcel to deliver and Edward shot out to look at the house. The van driver got back in the van and drove off before Edward could jump back inside. He couldn't remember where he had come from or quite what the van looked like. He wouldn't recognise the van driver again.

Every time a van arrived at the owner's house Edward would inspect it to see if it was *his* van, which would take him home, but it never was. He had now been at the owner's house for several years and no one had come to collect him.

At first, he had to live off killing mice and birds. And then he ventured into the owner's garden and tried to make her notice and like him. She called him 'Cat', which wasn't very imaginative. She didn't have a cat of her own. Edward told me he just lurked around in the garden, hoping the owner would take him in, but she ignored him. She put out the odd bowl of food but must have thought he lived somewhere else and had his own family.

One day the owner decided she would like a cat of her own and she came home from the Cat Rescue Centre with three cats. Edward couldn't understand why she would bring home three cats to live at her house when he so much wanted a home. He hadn't managed to explain that he wanted a home and was homeless, living on his wits and having to fend for himself.

The three new cats were big and fluffy and Edward thought they looked like farm cats. He didn't think they looked like proper house cats. For the first two weeks the cats were kept in the house. They didn't come out at all. Edward said that this is what happens when cats have new homes. They have to get used to a new place and a new owner before being allowed out to wander.

And then, after two weeks, the carpenter arrived to put in a cat flap, so that the three new cats could have a door

Edward is always in charge

of their own and venture out into the garden. Edward sat outside the door while the carpenter put in the cat flap. Soon it was finished. Edward wanted it to be *his* home and not their home. So when the cat flap was installed, Edward climbed through it.

'Hi, I'm Edward. You may think this is your home but I was here first.'

Edward didn't think the farm cats seemed very bright or interesting. He sidled up to the owner and did what cats do when they want to be endearing. He rubbed up against her legs and meowed. He looked up at her and tried to tell her he was *her* cat.

'Hello, Cat,' she said. 'What are you doing here?' Edward tried to tell her that he intended to stay. The next day she put Edward in a box in the car and took him to the vet's. The vet checked Edward to see if he had a microchip to say he belonged to someone else, but Edward's previous owners had never had him chipped, so there was no record of where he came from. Our owner says boy cats should always have a chip and a chop, whatever that means.

The owner hoped that Edward would mix with the three farm cats she had thought of adopting, but he was far superior to them. As Edward explained, he was going to stay and they wouldn't. Sure enough, the owner kept Edward and returned the three farm cats to the Cat Rescue Centre. The owner was now Edward's owner and Edward was now *her* cat.

He had always looked at cars and vans from that day on, just in case one was from his previous home. Once he thought he saw the van driver who had brought him here, but then he thought better of it. His home with the owner was better than his old home. He had a ready supply of mice and birds on the golf course, he had a hotel with a night manager who would keep him company and give him titbits at any time of the night. And now he had me.

Life for Edward was idyllic. And he was so respected that he even received letters from time to time, addressed to 'Sir Edward Saunders'. He was featured on a website about golf and a chapter entitled 'Edward the Golfing Cat' featured in a very famous golf book. Edward was a real VIP – a Very Important Puss.

When we got home, the day turned into a very special one. It was to be my first day on the golf course. My owner took Edward and me out to practise golf with her. Every day since

Edward loves his golf

my arrival, my owner had put a golf ball in front of my nose on the kitchen floor and forbidden me to touch it. On one occasion, I rebelled and nudged it towards the fridge. She took it away, shouted 'Leave' at me and then dabbed a foul-smelling substance on the ball, eucalyptus oil. I certainly never wanted to touch a golf ball again.

Now it was real. The owner had her clubs in a big bag, and attached my lead to the bag with a clip. She also had a couple of plastic tubes containing golf balls. These weren't like the ones I had been trained not to touch but were yellow and had her name on.

'They're just practice balls,' said Edward, wisely. 'She hits them up the field. You and I must stay very still and watch. Try to look interested in what she's doing but don't bother to watch the ball. Then we go off with her to find the balls, she picks them up and we all go back home. The real fun is if she loses a ball in thick grass or trees, and I go and hunt it out for her. You'll soon get the picture. As people say, you'll get in the swing of it. That's a pun on the word 'swing'. If you hear that old joke, try to look impressed.'

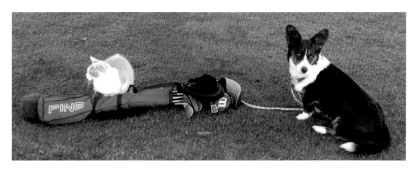

He doesn't have to have a lead!

'So why aren't you tied to the golf bag, Edward?' I said, as we walked out on to the golf course.

'Cats don't generally go on leads. That's because we're bright and intelligent and can find our way home without our owner's help. That's why we're allowed to wander.'

That sounded silly to me. After all, Edward had been lost because he climbed into a van as a kitten and arrived here. But I didn't like to question him. I still didn't quite trust him, and remembered Mum's words: 'Cats are loners; they don't even trust each other. Beware.'

Our owner tipped out all the golf balls in a heap and started to hit them. I sat and quivered. It was so exciting. I knew I mustn't ever touch a golf ball that sat still, but it would be such fun to charge after one. I watched Edward. Our owner had a funny furry cover on one of her golf clubs, which looked like a teddy bear, and Edward cuddled up to it. I began to see another side to Edward. He couldn't be all bad if he liked a teddy. Swish, swish, our owner would hit the balls away. Quite cleverly, the balls all seemed to go in the same direction, and I could see them in the distance. Then she hit one in a different direction and seemed a bit cross.

'That's when the fun starts,' said Edward. 'We'll stay out here until the ball's found. I usually go and look for stray golf balls with her. Sometimes it's nearly dark before she finds the very last one.'

'Why doesn't she have squeaking, talking balls like my red one? Then she could call to a lost one to say where it was.'

'You have to remember, Annika, that people don't think like we do. She does talk to the golf ball. I hear lots of golfers talk to their golf balls. But usually they only chastise a golf ball if it doesn't do what they want. You'll hear them call the ball a silly ball, or a stupid ball, and sometimes I have to flick my ears to make sure I don't hear nasty, rude words people shout at golf balls. I always assume that a golf ball treated like this will just hide and wait until a new owner finds it. Now, watch, Annika, and don't interrupt. You must remember that golfers like everything to be very, very quiet. You must never woof when a golfer is hitting. They find it quite off-putting.'

Our owner continued to hit all the balls into the distance. Then it was our big moment and Edward and I were taken to collect them. The owner prodded each ball with a tube that sucked them up. Edward was allowed to run freely. He would run up to a ball and stand beside it until the owner and I arrived. I was held firmly on the end of my lead and taken ball to ball while she collected them.

I couldn't really see that it was much fun. I nudged one with my nose but the owner shouted 'Leave' so loudly that I jumped with surprise. Eventually, she had every ball except two. 'That's two missing, Edward. Where do you think they are?'

He leapt off into the thick grass by some trees and jumped around. The grass tickled his tummy and I could see he was pretending to hunt for the missing balls. He found one. I didn't usually hear her talk much to Edward but the golf course was different. She talked to him there. He stared back at her and gave a tiny squeak.

'Oh, you *are* a good boy. Well done.' The owner took a little cat biscuit from her pocket and gave it to Edward.

I thought this looked a good game. What if I could find the other one? But it was quite difficult because I was still held tightly on the lead. We walked up and down, up and down, but there was no sign of the missing ball. I thought it might be worth shouting to it so I gave a woof, just a very little woof, but the ball didn't answer back and the owner didn't seem too pleased with me. Then I spotted it, yellow and gleaming and just asking to be found. I woofed again and tried to drag my owner over to the ball but she didn't take any notice.

'Edward, look over there. Can you see the ball?' But Edward was busy scratching in a sandpit and doing a poop.

'Oh, Edward, don't be a dirty boy. Come out of the bunker. Come on, help me find the last ball and then we can all go in for supper.'

I managed to alert Edward to the position of the stray ball and he walked over to it, coolly, confidently and calmly. With a flick of his tail he just sprang on to the ball and the owner praised him for finding it. He was such a show-off. I tried to explain to the owner that I had found it, but the more I woofed, the crosser she became.

'Right, now, Annika. Let's turn you into a real golfing dog.'

My owner told me to sit, which I dutifully did, just a little way away from her. I had by now been to a few puppy obedience classes and knew my 'sits' from my 'stands', my 'waits' and my 'comes', and even the word 'leave', although that took real willpower. Edward sat beside me, although he hadn't been told to. She put down one of the yellow golf balls. Oh my nose, my paws. Let me touch you. But I knew I mustn't. She took out one of her golf clubs and struck the golf ball just a very little way – not like her real shots – but just to tease, or train, me.

'LEAVE,' she shouted. My nose quivered with excitement and my paws just trembled to go after it, but I knew I mustn't. What would Mum do? She would do as she was told and so must I. I mustn't let her down. I mustn't let Mrs Cole down. I mustn't let Kiki or Toby or any of the rest of the family down. I ran just a very few steps. The little yellow ball was irresistible.

Then I stopped and turned and woofed a rather apologetic woof, and my owner shouted 'LEAVE.' I returned to her side. And then she walked to the ball and told me to sit again. I sat. I knew I must. And there was Edward just glaring at me. The owner hit the ball again and shouted 'LEAVE' but I so wanted to chase the ball. I stayed sitting and she praised me and gave me a biscuit. It was cheating really because it was only one of Edward's little cat biscuits, but still it felt good to succeed. She walked to the ball and we did it again and then again and each time I just sat. The temptation was so great. This was golf and I was going to be a great golfing dog.

'Please, please dear owner, can I chase the golf ball once, just once?' A little dog can resist most things but a running, jumping ball is a temptation too great. I was off. I couldn't help it. Something inside me just urged me to run after the ball.

My owner shouted after me but it was too late. I was sure I had broken the number-one rule for all great golfing dogs. I had followed the ball. I ran up to it, leaving Edward and

What temptation!

my owner many yards behind me. I bit the ball lovingly and sweetly, like I did my squeaking, talking ball, but it was hard to the touch and unpleasant. It was also very small and when I nudged it, it moved a few inches only. It was no real fun to play with.

I had two options. I had been wicked. I could sit by the ball and pretend nothing had happened or I could escape. Would my owner punish me for my disobedience? In that case, I must run away and hide. Or would she forgive me since it was my first time? My owner and Edward were storming towards me. I had dropped the ball and the owner was shouting, 'Good girl. Stay.' But Edward was telling me other things. 'You'll be in trouble when she catches you. Run, Annika, run.'

Oh, who to believe? I ran off, just in case Edward was right. But my owner, who sometimes wears a little badge saying 'I'm brighter than I look', had me sussed. There in her pocket was my squeaky, red, talking ball, the love of my life. She held the ball and it squeaked to me, 'Come back, Annika.' The owner threw the squeaky ball back towards the gate of the house and I followed its cry. I picked it up and cradled it gently in my mouth. Compared with a golf ball – all hard and nasty and unforgiving – the talking ball was a pleasure to hold. And then the owner gave me a biscuit, not just one of Edward's little ones, but a red one shaped like a heart.

I had loved my first day of golf. My owner picked up her golf bag and the two tubes of balls and we all returned to the house, Edward leading the way. His tail seemed to be even longer than usual and that little tell-tale curl just flicked as he walked, leaving me in no doubt who was really in charge of the whole operation.

We got back to the kitchen just as darkness fell. The owner put away her golf clubs and made our supper – biscuits and meat from a tin for me and just biscuits for Edward. She took his supper into the utility room and set out two bowls on the worktop. I always saw the owner put out two bowls of food for Edward. I had never asked Edward the reason. I assumed she wanted Spare Cat to come in for supper, even though Edward hated him so. Anyway, that was a question for another day.

The nasty black dragon was there to greet me at the end of the garden when I went out for a final walk. I was growing less frightened of it as the weeks went by. It never came across the water into the garden but just stared at me from the other side.

My owner came out to play with me for a few minutes. She sat on a bench and threw the squeaky ball. I gathered it into my mouth and returned it right to her feet. I woofed a special woof that meant, 'Throw it again.' She threw it again. I retrieved it again, right back to her feet, and I woofed the same throw-it-again woof. She threw it again and again and again. On and on until Edward spoiled the game by jumping on her lap, knocking over her cup of tea and allowing my talking ball to be abandoned.

That night, our owner was so pleased with me that she decided to take me upstairs to bed for a real treat. I had still only been upstairs once. There didn't seem any call to climb those stairs again. I heard strange noises up the stairs from time to time. Edward said the house was haunted but I think he was just trying to frighten me. Would I do better up the stairs this time? Up went the owner, so easily stair by stair. Up went Edward, leaping up two at a time. And then it was my turn. Remember what Mum said – stairs can be dangerous. Remember Mrs Cole's words of wisdom – slips and trips. Come on, Annika, you can do it. I was just that little bit longer and larger than when I last attacked the stairs, and I remembered how to do it. Up two stairs with the front paws, back paws on the next stair; up again with the front paws and follow with the back ones. Steadily, steadily, until I reached the top. Phew!

The owner was getting ready for bed and Edward was already making himself comfy in his grey hanging hammock on the radiator. He had a funny habit, which may be something all cats do, or perhaps it was just Edward. He would turn round and round in slow, steady circles until he had made himself quite comfortable, tucked in his tail, tucked in his paws, tucked in his nose but stuck out his whiskers. I could imagine he would soon be purring and snoring and lulling the owner and me to sleep.

I jumped up on the bed. It was quite a jump and I certainly wasn't getting off again. The owner's bed was very large. If we ever had visitors, I reckoned there was easily space for the owner and at least eight corgis. But somehow I managed to find my way right into the middle of the bed, so that I had most of it and the owner was almost falling off the edge. I was quite ready to settle down for the night but the owner had one last thing to do, just to watch the news on television. I pricked up my ears. 'The world's top woman golfer, Annika Sorenstam, who many consider the best woman golfer ever, has set a new women's world record with a score of 59.'

That's her, that's my namesake. It's *the* Annika. All my thoughts of golf came back to me. I mustn't let her down. I *must* be the best. Mum, dear Mum Maggie, how proud you would have been of me. I know I'll become a great golfing dog. I'll have my own website one day, just like Edward the cat.

Our owner switched off the television and I snuggled up tight against her, with my head right next to her head, sharing her pillow.

'Goodnight Annika.'

'Goodnight Owner. Goodnight Edward. Goodnight Mum Maggie, and golfing dogs everywhere.'

I thought I heard a little grunt from the radiator. 'And goodnight golfing cats – don't forget the golfing cats!'

Thank you, Edward.

6

Upstairs, Downstairs

As usual, Edward had disappeared to his next sleeping place by the time the owner and I woke up.

'Good morning, Annika.'

'Good morning, Owner.'

The owner was considerably more energetic than I was. She was soon up and away and I could hear her chatting to Edward in the kitchen. 'There's my good boy.'

Someone rang the doorbell. A man had come to cut the grass. The owner turned on the television downstairs. I just lay there on the bed, thinking of golf and daydreaming of football.

It's a cat's life!

The sun was streaming into the bedroom and I moved across the bed to find the sun. I had seen Edward use this trick and learnt it from him. He would find the very last patch of sunshine on the lounge carpet as the sun moved across the sky. Edward was really a very wise cat. I think he had learnt his wisdom from the radio. 'The sun always moves from left to right across the sky. Remember that, when you're looking for a good place to sleep in the garden.'

I could see out of the bedroom window and on to the golf course. I was tired after the previous day's activities and was idly wondering what the day had in store when I nodded off …

'Come on, Annika, you can't stay in bed all day. If you don't come downstairs, I'll have to leave you here.'

The owner was calling me from downstairs. I stretched. Would I ever grow as long as Mum Maggie? Up with the ears. Out with the tail. Nice shiny eyes. 'Yes, Owner, ready for action. Here I come.'

And then I remembered the stairs. This would be my second descent. On the first occasion, the owner had carried me down. Now I was left to conquer them on my own.

I crept to the top of the stairs. 'How on earth will I do these?' I thought, looking down in horror. It seemed a very long way. 'Slips and trips' – Mrs Cole's words of wisdom came back to me. And I remembered how Mr Cole had been so angry with Toby when he had ventured up the stairs as a very young puppy.

I gave a special woof, which meant that I was coming. But

how was I going to do the stairs? I put one front paw down on the top step. What next? It was like dipping it in the water that first time. I pulled it back quickly. OK, now let's work this out. Do I put both paws on the top step? Well then where do my back paws go? I can't stretch both front paws down two stairs. It isn't just the opposite from going upstairs. Come on, Annika. Think again. Left front paw forward. Back right paw on to the same step. There doesn't seem enough room for all of me. Oh, help. I could see myself tumbling head first down the whole flight of stairs. Mum Maggie had never been upstairs and never taught me about stairs. Edward wasn't here to show me. I tried again. Down with one paw, then another, a bit of a slither on my belly. I was down about four stairs and I was frightened. I was very, very frightened. I turned to climb back upstairs and had the shock of my life. There above me was another cat. She – I since found out it was a she – was now curled up on the top but one step. She had a huge tail and had hidden behind it, her yellow flashing eyes peering out over it.

'Good morning, Annika. I'm Sophie. I control the staircase in this house.'

I couldn't believe I had never seen her before. Where had she come from? This must be why there was always a second cat bowl on the worktop. It wasn't for Spare Cat; it was for Sophie. I chuckled to myself. There were three of them – Stare Cat, Spare Cat and Stair Cat. I laughed so much at my own silly joke that I tumbled a couple more steps down the staircase.

Sophie wanted to display her supremacy on the stairs. They were, after all, and as she had said, her domain. She controlled the staircase. She shot past me and sat menacingly three stairs below me. Now I couldn't get down. And the owner was continuing to call me. 'Come on, Annika. Quickly, very, very quickly. I'm going.'

I woofed a woof that meant wait for me. I woofed another woof that meant help. And then there was a third type of woof; this one meant I need you. But the owner didn't respond. I heard the back door shut. I was alone on the stairs with Sophie. And I didn't like it.

I couldn't turn round. I couldn't go up and I couldn't go down. I was well and truly stuck. There was nothing for it but to make friends with Sophie.

'Why have we never met? I've been here several weeks. Where have you been?'

But Sophie wasn't saying much. She was the one who made the odd noises I had heard upstairs. She slept most of the day in a spare bedroom and then went out to play at night, long after I was in bed. Yes, the second food bowl was for her. No, she didn't want to socialise. Yes, she controlled the staircase. Her favourite stair was the third from the top. She made me feel very silly asking why she was called Sophie. 'We are Edward and Sophie, like the royal family's Edward and Sophie.' Yes, she did go out on the golf course, but only after dark or just when it was getting dark. No, she would not let me downstairs. This was her staircase.

I was trapped, totally trapped. Should I go down and risk Sophie's anger and an accident or should I go back up. I decided to turn round and return to the top. And there I sat. I so wanted to have a wee. I crossed my legs and waited. Surely the owner would come back soon.

At last I heard her return.

'Annika, Annika.'

I woofed a here-I-am woof. And then a come-and-get-me woof. At last, she arrived at the bottom of the stairs. And there we were, with Sophie halfway down the stairs and me at the very top.

'Oh, you silly girl, Annika. You can come past Sophie. She's fine.'

I tried to explain that I couldn't do stairs. It wasn't just Sophie, though that added to the problem. I put my first paw down, then the next, then another. The owner suddenly realised the problem.

It's Sophie – keeper of the stairs!

'Oh, my poor bunny. You can't do stairs.'

She shooed Sophie away and came up to fetch me. She went slowly down the stairs backwards ahead of me. Finally, I rolled over and over down the last few steps but I had arrived. I did a little wee on the carpet at the bottom of the stairs and the owner wasn't very pleased. She went and got a rag and started rubbing the carpet. I grabbed the rag and pulled and tugged it and the owner put spray on the carpet. She was fairly furious and glared at me. And Edward walked past us and sniffed a very snooty sniff the way cats do. 'Cats don't do that sort of thing.'

And then Edward was sick. And I woofed a little serves-you-right woof.

And Sophie arrived in with a starling in her mouth and let it loose to fly around the hall. It crashed into a window. The owner rushed to open the window but the starling just went from picture frame to picture frame, curtain rail to curtain rail. It refused to go out of the window. Sophie jumped on a bookcase and knocked over some flowers. Edward continued to be sick.

'Thank heavens *you* are such a good girl, Annika.'

It taught me a very good lesson, which was to stand me in good stead for the rest of my life. Always make sure someone else is there to take the blame. I sat looking innocent and rather smug.

My misdemeanour was forgotten. The owner didn't know whether to grab Sophie, chase the starling or follow the vomiting Edward with a bucket, rag and spray.

7

Lost and Alone

As the days and weeks went on, I tried to get more practice going up and down stairs. I could never get to the very top because Sophie was usually sitting there. She was a gentle, sweet cat and never showed any signs of attacking me, like Edward did, but I still never felt brave enough to pass her on the stairs. Going up was quite straight forward. As I grew to my full height and length I could bound up, two at a time – coming down was still a problem. It was that very first, daring step that was so difficult. It meant stretching down not just to the next step but to the step beyond it. I didn't feel confident, but once I had started I had to keep going.

I spent most nights sleeping in the kitchen. My owner had bought me a really nice cage. Some silly visitors said it was rather cruel for a dog to have a cage. Far from it. The cage gave me a refuge. The owner couldn't get into it. I always had somewhere to hide. She bought me a large red-and-white, cartoon-character mouse. I know it was supposed to be a mouse but it didn't look like the little grey ones that Sophie brought in for presents. New visitors to the house would often buy me cuddly toys but Mouse was always my favourite.

New visitors would always ask the same questions. 'What is she? Is she a cross between a collie and a dachshund? No,

Meet my beloved red mouse

I think she's a cross between a donkey and a dachshund. Ha ha. Oh, she's a Cardigan corgi. I didn't know there was such a thing. I've never seen a corgi that colour. I thought they were pale brown, like the Queen has.'

My owner was very good at explaining about Cardigan corgis and Pembroke corgis.

'The Cardigan corgi is larger than the Pembroke. They come in all sorts of colours. Although Annika looks black and white, she's actually what's technically called a tricolour brindle. Cardigan corgis have these huge ears and slightly turned out toes, and should be quite a bit bigger than a Pembroke. They're really bred to drive a herd of cattle. You can just imagine Annika walking fourteen miles a day, driving cattle from Wales to market at Ludlow.'

Mum Maggie – very different from Pembrokes!

I'd heard it all before and was looking forward to seeing my first Pembroke corgi!

Every now and then my owner would let me sleep upstairs with her. Even though that meant dodging and weaving past Sophie to get upstairs, it was worth it. My owner obviously had the same ideas about stairs as Mrs Cole – 'Remember, Annika, slips and trips and stairs can be dangerous.' My owner always made me sit at the top of the stairs and wait until she was at the bottom. She would leave me parked at the top on the landing, usually raise her right hand and say, 'Wait.' And I learned to wait and to wait and to wait. And then, when she got to the bottom, she would turn towards me and shout, 'All right.'

It was quite a game, but it did make the stairs safe for both of us.

Although Sophie would sit menacingly on the stairs, she never did me any harm. She just peeped out from behind her silly, fluffy tail. I'm sure she thought that if she couldn't see me, I couldn't see her.

Edward, who really is a very wise cat, explained that Sophie is like an ostrich. An ostrich, as Edward told me, is a daft bird that hides its head in the sand, and then because it can't see anything, assumes that other people can't see it. That sounded pretty much like Sophie. I wondered if we would ever see an ostrich in our garden.

Edward is quite a bird-watching enthusiast. I would see him peeping out from behind the shed, watching the birds. His favourite game was to lie down in long, thick grass and creep up on a bird slowly and surely until it flew away. Every now and then Edward would catch a bird and in whatever skirmish they had, Edward would usually win.

Once I saw him do something very naughty indeed. A mummy duck was walking across the lawn from the water towards another pond on the golf course. She had ten little ducklings walking behind her. Edward took the last one and then there were nine. I didn't see what happened. I don't expect he hurt the duckling but I never saw it again. When the mummy duck came back Edward again took the last duckling and now she had eight. Eventually, they had all gone. I like to think Edward adopted them.

Edward could do lots of things that I couldn't do, and I could do quite a few things that he couldn't. Edward would sit at the bottom of a tree and then rush up it as fast as possible.

Sometimes he would chase a bird; sometimes he would chase a squirrel. I had to sit at the bottom, watching him. Squirrels seem to be able to step farther along branches than Edward could. It was fun to see squirrels teasing Edward. They would walk out along the branch and the branch would bounce up and down but Edward had to stay at the thick end and couldn't follow all the way. The squirrel would be laughing at Edward, and he didn't like it. One day I saw Edward catch a squirrel; the squirrel wasn't very amused then, but at least he got away.

When Edward and I went out to play golf with our owner, it always really irritated me that Edward didn't have to go on a lead. We did lots more golf practice together, Edward sitting on the owner's golf bag, me attached to it by a lead. We'd help her pick up the balls and then it would be my turn to play the game of sitting and waiting, off my lead, while she hit the ball forward. It was just so tempting to rush after a ball but I knew I mustn't. I was taught to sit in a special place just to her side so that she could watch me and I could watch her. She always hit little shots while I was off the lead and I longed for the day when she would trust me while she hit big shots. And then we got to the green, which is a special part of the course, very, very closely mown, where she would putt the ball towards the hole. I had to sit just off the edge of the green and was never, ever allowed to walk on it.

By contrast, Edward would be really annoying and often get in the way of the ball. When the ball went in the hole, Edward repeatedly tried to fish it out with his paws. He used to get ever more furious but never did manage to take the ball out on his own.

One day, my owner took Edward and me much farther on to the golf course than usual. I was still tied to the golf bag and sat quietly every time she hit the ball or when we got to the green. As usual, my nose would quiver with excitement and my paws would tremble with enthusiasm just wanting to go after the ball.

Then she hit the ball very hard and far and I couldn't resist running after it. I still had the little bag of golf clubs attached to the end of my lead and they came, too. My owner shouted, 'Annika, Annika, leave.' But I was off. Edward came bounding after me. The golf bag got lighter and lighter as one club fell out and then another until just one club was left. Eventually, I came to a stream and I was going so fast I couldn't stop, so

I ran off with the golf bag!

I jumped over it. The last club fell out and plopped into the water, and I had this awful feeling of impending doom.

'Go on, Annika,' shouted Edward. 'You'll be in dreadful trouble now.' Edward sat still and I just kept on running. I didn't look round to see if our owner was following. I could hear her shouting, 'Annika, Annika,' but I knew I had done something terribly wrong and I didn't dare go back. When I finally stopped and turned round, the little blue golf bag still attached to the end of my lead, I could just about see the owner clambering down into the stream to fish out her last golf club.

What was I going to do? What would Mum Maggie do? What would Toby or Emily do? But more to the point, what was I going to do? I was quite puffed from my long run and I

It's Darcy the Pembroke Champion without a tail

and now they are allowed tails again!

decided the only thing to do was to hide, so I crept in among some trees. I thought of Edward's ostrich and right now it didn't seem so daft. Maybe if I couldn't see the owner, she wouldn't be able to see me. I lay down behind a log and stayed and stayed and stayed some more. I could hear the owner calling for me. By now, it was getting quite dark and suddenly I really hoped that she would find me. I went round the tree to look in another direction. Perhaps she was over there, but no she wasn't. So I went on round to the front of the tree and hid down behind the log again.

And then I realised that I was stuck. I'd wound the golf bag and the lead round and round the tree a couple of times and I couldn't move far. I could hear the owner calling for me but she seemed to be going farther in the other direction, because her calls were quieter. I decided I would have to shout for her. First I did a here-I-am woof. And then it became a help-I'm-frightened woof. She didn't come. I could feel I was going to start whimpering and sobbing because I thought I might be lost out on the golf course forever. So I gave a little please-come-and-get-me woof. Still she didn't come. And then I spotted Edward. Cats don't usually run a long way fast but they do seem to be quite adventurous creatures.

'Look, Edward. If you will rescue me and get our owner to come and find me, I'll teach you how to get a golf ball out of the hole. I've worked it out.'

'Well, Annika, I don't really believe you. How do you think you can get a ball out of a hole if I can't?'

I was just about to tell Edward and then I realised that if I told him there would be no incentive for him to rescue me.

'I'm not that silly, Edward. If I tell you, you won't bother to get my owner.'

'Excuse me, Annika. She's our owner. In fact, she was my owner until Sophie came along and then you came along. All right, just wait here and I'll see if she's interested in coming to get you.'

He could really be quite beastly. Off he wandered in his very slow, steady way, showing no degree of urgency. He couldn't resist stopping on the way, climbing into a bunker and scratching up the sand and doing another poop. To Edward, the whole golf course was covered with giant litter trays. He never had a litter tray in the house, so why he had to poop in bunkers I don't know. But that was just Edward.

After a very long time, when it was almost dark, I could see the owner in the distance, shining a big torch and shouting, 'Annika, Annika.' At last she was within earshot. I did another here-I-am woof, followed by a come-and-get-me woof and then an I'm-ever-so-pleased-to-see-you woof.

The owner was not very pleased with me at all. She was cold and hungry. I was cold and hungry. I learnt later that she never found one of her golf clubs that fell out of the bag.

I gave a little I'm-terribly-sorry woof but she didn't respond. That was followed by a please-let-me-try-again woof but again there was no response. I knew that I had been terribly naughty but I didn't realise the consequences.

Later, back at home, I heard my owner talking on the telephone. 'Is this Miss Ingrid's School of Correction? Yes, I

but no one has a tail as grand as Sophie's

73

have an extremely naughty dog, just a terribly naughty dog. She's ashamed and I'm ashamed and really I can't do anything with her. I'm told you're the best person to deal with a horribly disobedient animal.'

Silence.

'What do you mean if the dog is disobedient, it's the owner's fault? No, this dog is disobedient. If I told you the terrible thing she's done today, I'm sure you'd be shocked. No, she doesn't chase sheep. No, she doesn't chase cattle or geese. She chases golf balls … Well, I do think it's a serious problem. So you think I'm the one who needs training and not Annika. Well, we'll see about that. I'm told you're the best. When can Annika and I come and see you? And how long will we come for? Oh, you want us there for two days? Well yes, this dog is seriously unruly, and if I told you what a dreadful thing she's done today, you'd probably say you want her there for a whole six weeks. Yes, we'll arrive on Monday. It'll cost how much? My goodness, for that amount I could buy another dog. Well, yes, as you say, if I bought another dog, I'd just have two naughty dogs instead of one really good one. I'll see you on Monday.'

I sat in my cage horrified that I was going to be taken to Miss Ingrid's School of Correction in the Lake District. My owner might not have heard much about this establishment but it was legendary in the dog world. One of the advantages of having huge, stick-up ears is that they act like radar. My owner needed a mobile phone to talk to somebody two hundred yards away; my ears picked up messages from all over the place and the threat of being sent to Miss Ingrid's School of Correction was something we all knew only too well. I heard that she didn't allow dogs to have cuddly toys and they certainly weren't allowed biscuits as either bribery or reward.

I cuddled up in my cage, my head on red-and-white Mouse. I really couldn't have Miss Ingrid taking Mouse away from me. I think I had learnt my lesson about not getting lost, without having to go to the School of Correction. At least I was shut in my cage and Edward couldn't get in with me. He stood outside, taunting me, and thrust his right paw into my cage, with the nasty claws sticking right out.

'Remember, Annika, I'm in charge in this house. You don't really need Miss Ingrid's School of Correction. You just need Sir Edward's School of Correction. A swift clout from me and you will do what you're told. Remember, there's no hiding from Sir Edward. If you upset me, I'll turn into Muhammad Ali, the greatest boxer the world has ever known. Float like a butterfly, sting like a bee.'

'Don't be so horrid. Who saves you from the Sparc Cat? And don't forget I have the secret of how to get a golf ball out of a hole. One day, if you're a very sweet cat, I'll show you how to do it.'

Edward jumped up on to my cage and spent the night sleeping on it, leaving just the very tip of his tail hanging menacingly through the mesh. One large, green eye opened and closed every now and then, just to keep me in my place.

I felt very ashamed. My golfing career was over through naughtiness. I was dreading my trip to Miss Ingrid's School of Correction and wondered what on earth lay in store for me.

8

In Trouble Again!

I had three days of freedom before being taken to Miss Ingrid's School of Correction, and I was going to make the best of them. I woke up the morning after the golf-course incident to find that Edward had climbed off the top of my cage and disappeared without my even hearing. That's one of the great things about cats. They can move so silently and creep up on things. It would be nice to take Edward by surprise, just as he does rabbits and ducklings.

My owner came downstairs and opened my cage, and I tried to look as sweet and innocent as possible.

'How are you this morning, Annika? Let's go and have a good long walk.' This was music to my ears. I remembered those words of wisdom from Mum, tipped my head on one side and looked straight up at my owner, just to let her know that I understood every word she said.

'You are a good girl.'

'Yes, Owner, but not for long.'

Something told me I was going to be in trouble again because there was so much temptation around. I supposed I would have my usual light breakfast of a few biscuits. Sometimes I would be given an extra bowl of milk, but I didn't think today was going to be a good day. And then Edward arrived. The owner, and some of her friends, always said that Edward wanted to be a dog because he did dog-like things. Whenever Edward heard this, he was furious.

'Why on earth would I want to be like a dog? Dogs have to go on leads and are far more restricted than cats. I can jump on worktops and do my own thing while dogs have to be obedient. You know what they say, Annika. Dogs have masters and cats have servants.'

I didn't really understand what Edward meant but he is a very wise cat indeed. I decided to spend the journey to Miss Ingrid's figuring out all of Edward's words of wisdom.

Anyway, today he did a very clever thing. I mentioned before how our food is kept in the pantry. The house where we live seems very old and the door to the pantry must have been there for hundreds of years. Edward stood up against the door, lifted his paws towards the door handle and pushed out his claws. He started to claw very gently at the pantry door and I could see he had done this before.

'Now stop that Edward. Are you telling me you want some sardines?'

Edward didn't have to answer – the owner knew exactly what he wanted. Out came one of those magic tins, the little oblong ones with the funny pull-off lid. Yes, yes, yes. We were going to get sardines for breakfast. The good thing about a tin of sardines is that once the lid is off it doesn't shut again properly. So, once open, someone would have to eat the sardines. Edward would only eat sardines totally fresh out of the tin; Sophie would have just a teaspoonful and I absolutely adored them. I saw the owner put three bowls on the worktop. There was my big metal bowl, a little plastic bowl for Edward and a little tin bowl for Sophie. Off came the lid and she shared out the sardines. Edward, of course, was all round her on the worktop and she could hardly keep his nose out of the little tin while she opened it. In fact, once she had opened the tin and moved a couple of paces to get a fork, Edward was already licking the sardines, his tail quivering with excitement.

It was funny really. If I ever licked anything, like the day I was caught licking a piece of cheese, the owner would certainly never eat it, but somehow it seemed all right for Edward to lick the sardines and for me still to be given them. Anyway, that was something to ponder on the long journey to Miss Ingrid's.

The owner put a little bit of sardine into Edward's bowl and he was in raptures as he ate it. She put a little bit in the other bowl for Sophie. I was quite certain that Edward wouldn't eat it all. He had such a delicate appetite and knew when to stop.

'Ah,' I thought to myself, 'the rest of it must all be for me.' The owner added a forkful of sardines to my biscuits but the rest stayed in the tin. She put my bowl on the floor and almost before she could stand up I had scoffed the lot. Sardines really are quite lovely. And then I saw her wrap the sardine tin in cling film and pop it back in the fridge. Yippee, I thought, there must be more for me for later.

I was beginning to learn more about the housework. One of the owner's visitors called her the Domestic Goddess. I didn't quite know what that meant. I thought it might be a joke, because every time someone called my owner 'Domestic Goddess' they seemed to chuckle. The owner has a bookshelf, just at eye level for me, with lots of cookery books. Edward is far better at reading than I am and says that the books explain how to bake cakes and cook stews and pasta (whatever that is) and make soup and puddings. Edward says that five of the cookery books are specifically for cats' meals, but I think he may be teasing me. Edward says that the best cookery book on the shelf, and the one the owner uses most, is called *Good Mousekeeping*. I know that mice are very important to our owner. I remembered the day when Edward caught a mouse and released it in her bedroom, and she screamed and jumped on the bed. Perhaps that was a kind of mouse worship.

Anyway, I had never seen the owner take any of these books off the shelf. The only one she ever used was *Delia Smith's Cookery Course*. I could always spot this one on the bookshelf because, as a puppy, I'd pulled it on to the floor and eaten most of its cover. It had a nice, soft cover to chew where most of the others were hard. The owner had forgiven me and was probably pleased that I'd shown an interest in her cookery book.

My favourite item in the kitchen is the dishwasher. Once everyone has eaten, she stacks all the dirty plates and cups and knives and forks in the dishwasher and the clever machine washes them. I do wish she wouldn't turn it on at night, though. It makes a really nasty noise while I'm trying to sleep. The plates always come out sparkling and clean in the morning with not a trace of food. But when they go in at night, that's my

I could just lick them all clean

time to strike. The owner puts plates in the bottom and usually leaves the door open while she puts cups and glasses in the top. That's my window of opportunity to have a quick snatch of any leftovers on the plates. In fact, I can lick a plate so clean and leave it so sparkling that really she doesn't need a machine at all. If she thought sensibly, like a dog or a cat would, she could leave the plates on the floor for me to clean and just put the knives and forks and glasses and mugs in the machine.

I was looking at Edward's tongue the other day. His is quite different from mine. My tongue is large and soft, and when my owner wears shorts, I sometimes lick her legs and she doesn't seem to object. But Edward's tongue is very, very rough. In a moment of weakness, I once let him lick me on the side of my nose. It felt just like the sandpaper the carpenter used. I haven't told you about the sandpaper. The table in the kitchen has six chairs, and their legs look very like my chews. One morning, when I was feeling particularly bored and didn't have a chew, I tried nibbling one of the chair legs instead. Bits came off but didn't taste very nice. I thought if I kept on nibbling, I might get to some tasty bits in the middle. I've had chews like that where the outside doesn't taste very good but inside there are nice, meaty bits. Sadly, the chair leg didn't have any tasty bits. I'd been rather silly over this. I'd chosen a back leg, which was there for everyone to see. If I'd gone into the corner, I could have tried nibbling a less visible chair leg without anyone noticing.

The owner called in the handyman to repair the chair leg, and that's when I first encountered sandpaper. He rubbed down the chair leg and then stained it so that it looked almost as good as new again, just a bit narrower than the others. He put the chair in the corner, next to the wall, so that no one could see what I'd done.

Anyway, Edward's tongue and sandpaper are much the same. I heard the owner say so when Edward tried to wake her one morning by licking her eyelids. She certainly woke up pretty smartly, and screamed at him.

Most of the other interesting things in the kitchen are up on the worktop, Edward's worktop. I don't like the microwave or the kettle or the toaster. They all have specific jobs to do, which last a couple of minutes. When they're done, they scream at the owner to remind her that they've finished. The kettle makes a click and a whistle, the toaster makes a ping as the toast pops up and the microwave makes a loud ding. The problem with the microwave is that if she forgets to open its door, it makes another ding, and another ding, and another ding to remind her. She forgets about my very sensitive ears. Why have wonderful ears like mine for hearing things miles away and then bombard them with unpleasant noises?

And then there's a special cooking hob for warming pans of food. Edward said she put in this one, called an induction hob, especially for cats. It's an intelligent hob that gets hot only when a saucepan is placed on it. Edward explained that he can walk right across it and never get burnt. That's its great advantage over the old one and Edward says he can't understand why the makers of induction hobs don't use cats to advertise their products.

Oh, Edward is such a very wise cat. I'm sure if people could understand him he could be prime minister and run the country really well. He's always telling me there should be a National Health Service for animals, so that we could get free care. As Edward says, people are able to earn money and can pay for medical care. Animals are limited in what they can earn and need to get healthcare free.

Edward feels there should be a minimum pay scale for working cats and dogs, and that they should have paid annual holidays, like all other workers. I'm sure he would make a good minister for transport, ensuring that all roads have sidewalks or pavements especially for dogs, and of course, more bins for scooped poop. And, as Edward says, he wouldn't have got lost when the van brought him to the owner's house if signposting had been better.

Edward would also love to be in charge of planning. His first dictum would be that all houses must have cat flaps. He's heard of cats who have to stay indoors because their owners don't have cat flaps. He thinks it's demeaning to have to ask to go out. Personally, I think there should be dog flaps to allow dogs the same freedom but Edward and I don't see eye to eye on that one.

If Edward did run the country, I could be the minister for sport, and play football. I'd make sure that all sports grounds allocated special seating areas for dogs (and cats), just like they do for the disabled. And I do object to those notices that say no dogs can go in shops unless they are guide dogs or assistance dogs. It seems to me to be a form of discrimination that should be stamped out. This certainly would be stopped if Edward was prime minister.

Sophie could be the minister for education. She has some very good ideas and always describes it as 'catastrophic' when she hears people on the radio using bad grammar.

And Edward says that if he was the foreign secretary he would keep Great Britain for the British – no German shepherds or Rottweilers or French poodles or Siberian huskies. He says he would allow in dachshunds, though, because he quite respects them. In fact, Edward has many thoughts on home rule and independence for Scotland and thinks that Skye terriers should have to have passports to come into England. He does bat on about things. As foreign secretary, he would definitely ban Siamese cats because, he says, blue eyes on a cat really are unacceptable.

Anyway, I couldn't understand why the owner wasn't springing into action to take me for my walk until I realised that the housekeeper/cleaner was expected. I knew this was the case because the owner would always tidy up first. I think she must have been afraid of the housekeeper because she would always put things away and clean the kitchen before the housekeeper arrived. Edward says that the main advantage of a housekeeper's visit is to make you do things yourself and bring some discipline to the house.

The housekeeper uses a machine that Edward always refers to as a vaccy. The owner calls it a vacuum cleaner and probably knows best; the housekeeper calls it the Hoover. In fact, we have three of them in the house, one for upstairs, one for downstairs and a little tiny one for doing Sophie's domain on the stairs themselves. Edward says that he doesn't think our owner can use the vaccy because in all the years he has been here, he has never seen her using it. Edward hates the vaccy because it makes a terrible noise. I hate the vaccy because the housekeeper always sings as she pushes it around. What a racket the two of them make!

With my trip to Miss Ingrid's School of Correction looming, I thought I might as well go for any sort of bad behaviour now and get it over with, so I tugged and pulled at the cord of the vaccy and the plug came out of the wall. Suddenly, we were left with the housekeeper's singing and one dead vaccy. She plugged it in again and off she went. But as all very perceptive cats and dogs know, the vaccy has attachments that can be quite fun. There is a little one with a tube and a brush and it

Somehow this arrived in the garden!

was quite a good game to bite all the bristles out of the brush until it was bald. Then I thought that maybe this game would be construed as rather naughty, so I ran out into the garden and dropped the bald brush into a flower bed, out of sight.

The owner wasn't taking much notice of me, so I decided to make my own amusement. I don't really know quite what happened but suddenly I found myself with a big, red plastic watering can in my mouth. It was fun to play with and made comical, musical noises as I blew down the tube. I put it in the middle of the lawn for safekeeping. Then I noticed a large, black plastic flowerpot. I grasped it at one edge and ran off with it, which was great fun because I couldn't see where I was going. I gave myself a little dare. How many paces could I run without losing my nerve, stopping and putting it down

Blow hard and it makes lovely tunes!

and peeping around the side of the pot? I soon learnt to focus on the other end of the lawn, pick up the flowerpot and run. I could gauge pretty well when I got to the other end and got quite confident. That was a really good game. I decided to put the black flowerpot next to the red watering can, just so I would remember where they were.

How far can I run in a bucket!

I was just tidying up in the garden

Next, I spotted a pair of green gloves that the gardening lady had left by a flower bed. They smelt a bit funny and I thought there must be something interesting inside them. I tugged at one and parts of it seemed to come away in my teeth. It seemed a shame to have one green glove in bits and the other intact. Best to try to make them a matching pair again. I started to rip bits off the other glove but they just wouldn't look the same as each other. I got a bit bored with them and left them with the black flowerpot and the red watering can.

The owner had put a clever sprinkling gadget on the lawn, which sprayed water from side to side. It was on and I thought it might be fun to show off to Edward, who hates water, and dance in and out of the sprinkler. But it wasn't very interesting.

The sprinkler had been in the same place for quite a long time and I knew that the owner liked to move it around the garden to water other parts of the lawn. I had just meant to be helpful but as I pulled the sprinkler along, on the end of the yellow hose, the sprinkler itself fell off and I was left with

Oh dear!

just the hose, which was a bit unreliable and had a mind of its own. As I pulled it in one direction it flicked back, rather like Edward's tail, and pointed in the opposite direction, spraying water as it went. Never mind, the owner wanted water on the lawn.

Still the owner didn't come to play with me. I could see a big, blue plastic bucket full of twigs and leaves that the gardener had cleared up. I knew they had to be put on the compost heap at the end of the garden behind the shed. It seemed a shame to leave my owner to do this when she was obviously busy, so I dragged the bucket over towards the compost heap. By the time I got it there, lots of the twigs and leaves had jumped out by themselves and were lined up behind me on the grass. Still, a few were left in the bucket, so I shook it and shook it and shook it again and most of them fell out. I needed the owner to realise just how hard at work I had been, so I dragged the blue bucket back to the red watering can, the black flowerpot, the green gloves and the yellow hose, which, although uncontrollable, was mostly where I had put it.

I'd watched a programme on television about sheepdogs rounding up sheep. I didn't have any sheep. I only had a red-and-white furry mouse, a black-and-blue dragon, a furry monkey and a pink teddy. But at least I could practise with all these things in the garden and I was sure the owner would be pleased. Well, actually, I didn't think the owner would be pleased. I thought it was probably bad behaviour. But in my own mind I could excuse it because I was trying to adapt to new skills.

One thing I could do to please her before she came out. The housekeeper had hung some sheets on a twiddly twirly thing to dry. On a windy day, like today, it was supposed to spin around so that the wind got inside the sheets. I thought I could probably dry things a bit faster by hanging on to the bottom end of one sheet and running round in circles to spin the dryer. I noticed that I had chosen a faulty one. Yes, the sheet I had chosen unfortunately had a few holes in it. So I chose another one and decided to run with that. After a time I realised that that one, too, had some little holes and what looked like blood on the corner of the sheet. I thought the owner would be quite cross because she would think the housekeeper hadn't washed them very well.

I was getting a little bit bored by now. The owner had been

And this one really wasn't my fault

making coffee and talking on the phone and not paying much attention to me.

And then it was the best moment of the day. The postman arrived in his little red van. He always brought me a biscuit or two and made a really big fuss of me. We have a letterbox outside the house on a post. Today, instead of just putting the mail in the letterbox, he took it to the back door. He handed me one letter, which he seemed to know wasn't very important, and then rang the doorbell. The owner had to sign for a special letter. He didn't mean to tell tales on me, because he is a really good postman, but somehow he just blurted out that there seemed to be a bit of a mess on the back lawn.

I felt very ashamed and thought of jumping in his van and escaping like Edward had done from his home when he was a kitten. My owner shouted, 'Annika,' louder than I had ever heard her shout before. The housekeeper was standing behind her, broom in hand.

'Oh help. I think I'm in trouble.'

By this time the postman had run to the gate and was reversing his van at great speed, unfortunately with Edward sitting on its roof. Edward escaped with a mighty jump on to the back fence and sidled off in the opposite direction. He was going to be no support to me at all.

Neither my owner nor the housekeeper were pleased. My owner took me inside, locked me in my cage – thank goodness to be somewhere safe – and then picked up the phone.

Love is a bright blue Frisbee

'Is that Miss Ingrid's School of Correction? I've just received the signed-for letter with instructions. I was bringing Annika to see you for two days on Monday. I did say that two days should be enough to get rid of the bad behaviour but now I'm not sure. We'd like to come for three days and then could I book her in for a two-week residential course on her own three weeks later. Yes, I know you say it's my fault if she misbehaves, but really if you saw the destructive things this dreadful dog has done, I'm sure you would agree that it's the dog and not me. Yes, I know Cardigan corgis are a very rare breed. If they behave like this, there isn't much wonder there's very little call for them. Yes, we'll look forward to seeing you on Monday and if she can't improve, I'm afraid we may have to find a new home for her.'

I was just bitterly, bitterly disappointed.

And then she let me out of my cage, put me in the back of the car and said we were off to see a new friend, Barney, a golden retriever who might teach me some discipline.

9
My Friend Barney

I wasn't a very happy girl when I first met Barney. I love my home in the middle of the golf course. I was beginning to love Edward with his rough tongue, his vicious claws, his arrogant walk and his menacing tail. That makes him sound quite unpleasant but, as cats go, I should think he's in the top league. I also loved Sophie, although I didn't see her very often. She stopped me going upstairs if I wanted to go up and she stopped me coming downstairs if I wanted to come down, but I really didn't want to be sent away to a new owner.

Would I like Barney? We met Barney and his owner for the first time to go for a walk near a lake with some woods.

Barney was quite the handsomest dog I had ever seen – a golden retriever. I'd never seen one of them before. He was huge and had a rather gruff bark, which was just a nice-to-meet-you woof.

'Yes, and nice to meet you, too, Barney.' I told him that I was being sent away to Miss Ingrid's School of Correction the following Monday and needed to learn some good manners from him before I went.

'Don't worry, Annika, I'll look after you. Just follow me.'

Barney went off at quite a speed, left, right, left, right, and I found it quite difficult to keep up with him. And then

My friend Barney

temptation got the better of me again. I know it was the thought of going to the School of Correction that was bringing out the worst in me. I didn't want to follow Barney. I wanted to make Barney go where I wanted to go. I think it's the instinct of all herding dogs to be in control, but from behind. Barney stopped for a moment and I nuzzled up, just to his left side. I gave his fur a little nip and decided that we would go right round the lake. I just pushed him along. I drove him along. I herded him along. I decided exactly where Barney and I were going and that's where we went. I was firmly in control. I just hung on his left side, tweaked his fur from time to time and drove him along at just the right speed. This would be brilliant practice for the first time I had my own herd of cattle to move. I had done herding with the red watering can, the black flowerpot, the green gloves, the yellow hose and the blue bucket. Now this was for real.

'Come on, Barney, run along. There's a good boy. No, turn to the right round this corner and keep on going.'

By this time, my owner and her friend had decided it wasn't worth following us and I could see them on the other side of the lake. My owner seemed to be shouting something but because I was going at such a speed I couldn't really hear. Her friend was waving her arms and shouting to Barney. There was a chance I could have turned him right round and made him go back the way we had come, but I chose to keep moving him forward. I kept driving him, herding him, pushing him; I showed who was boss. Eventually, we arrived back to our owners, Barney at the front and me pushing him from behind.

I thought Barney's owner was quite ridiculous. She kept saying how good Barney had been, going at a steady pace so that I could follow.

'What a gentleman to keep his eye on her and make sure she got safely back to us.'

She thought I was following him. She hadn't got a clue that I was in control.

Barney, of course, is a retriever. He explained to me that he was supposed to collect things and bring them back. His owner decided to give us a demonstration of Barney's retrieving skills. My owner did explain that I was very good with a ball and would retrieve it and bring it back to her feet but I didn't get a chance. Barney's owner had a special plastic gadget for flinging the ball long distances. I could see the ball in the ball slinger and realised what was going to happen. Yes, yes, yes. My nose twitched and my paws quivered ready for the chase.

And then his owner turned and threw the ball into the lake. Well, I certainly wasn't going in there. Barney dived in and swam out to the ball, collected it in his mouth and swam back to the edge. If his owner thought I was going to get wet, she had another think coming. She leant forward into the lake, picked out the ball and threw it again for Barney. Off he went, paddle paddle, until he reached the ball. Personally, I'd always had problems with my squeaky ball and as soon as I tried to collect it, I seemed to nudge it farther away from me. So I watched Barney intently. He put his mouth right round the ball, gathered it up and swam back to the edge.

'Please, please let me have a go on dry land.' But they didn't take any notice. Barney's owner threw the ball out again and Barney rushed off and brought it back to the edge.

This time, I was there to meet him. I grabbed the ball off him and ran away with it. Barney looked disappointed, his owner looked disappointed and my owner laughed. She called to me to come back but I wasn't going to fall for that one and lose my ball. And then I thought, 'No, I'll show you who's the retriever round here.' I ran back to my owner and placed the ball right there at her feet. I sat down, looked up into her eyes, tilted my head just to the right (like Mum Maggie had always told me to do) and won her over once again.

It's mine and I won't give it back!

I thought my owner and Barney's owner might come to blows over the ball but it was Barney's ball and my owner had forgotten to bring mine. His owner flung it out into the middle of the lake again for Barney and I just sat on the side waiting. This time Barney wanted to make absolutely sure that I didn't grab the ball, and he knew I wasn't going to get wet. So he leapt up on to the bank and went right up to his owner to give her the ball. And then he shook and he shook and he shook some more. And there was water everywhere. She was drenched and my owner was drenched and I just sat like little Miss Perfect taking it all in.

'Oh Barney, you've made us filthy. Let's go and take you both off to the recreation ground and you can both enjoy the ball.'

My owner lifted me into the back of our car ready to drive off, but Barney wouldn't get in his car. He sat on the ground and looked up at it. He was much too heavy to lift. (My owner actually explained to some people a few months later that this is why a Cardigan corgi is such a good choice. We're big enough to be fun but small and light enough to pick up and pop in a car.) Barney just sat there. His owner tried to encourage him into the car with a biscuit, then with the ball, but he wasn't having any of it. She shouted at him. Suddenly, perfect Barney wasn't so perfect after all.

'Do you know, I've had six different cars since I've had Barney? We've tried a Honda, a Mercedes, a Lexus, another Honda, a Volvo and now the Range Rover. He got car sick in the Volvo. I didn't like the Honda. He was afraid of the self-shutting door of the Lexus and now he seems to be telling me that the Range Rover is too high.'

My owner joined in the task of getting Barney back into the car. Both of them tried to lift him but he just wriggled and protested. My owner had another idea and climbed into the back of the Range Rover to see if he would follow. But Barney still wouldn't get into the car.

'Is his birthday in May?' my owner asked. 'I do believe in star signs for dogs, just as for people, and those born in May can be terribly stubborn.'

'No, Barney has a birthday in August, and he's the perfect gentleman. Think of him as Leo the Lion. He's just somehow afraid of getting in cars.'

By this time my owner had jumped out of the car and they were both scratching their heads deciding what to do. Then my owner suggested that perhaps they would like to come to Miss Ingrid's School of Correction, too, if we could ever get Barney in the car. Perhaps she could deal with that problem. Again I thought they were going to argue.

'Barney is absolutely perfect. He doesn't need any form of training at all. It's just a question of choosing the right car to suit him.'

I thought to myself that if his owner turned on the ignition, he'd probably think he was going to be left behind and he might jump in. I tried to convey this with a turn-on-the-ignition-and-start-the-car woof. But they didn't understand. Then my owner, who could probably read my mind, suggested that Barney's owner should turn on the ignition and start the car. She did just that, Barney jumped into the car, my owner shut the back of it and off we went to the recreation ground.

When we got there, I told Barney I thought he was ridiculous, and he explained that what he really wanted was to have a harness and sit on the front seat, like he saw other dogs do. But he had never managed to explain this to his owner. I told him I thought he should use more initiative and next time he saw an advert for a car harness in a magazine, he should plonk it on his owner's lap.

Barney's owner, having retrieved the ball from the car, told my owner that Barney would, of course, be very quick chasing the ball, and she doubted whether I would manage to get it. I may have short legs and a long body but when the chips are down, I sure can run. I take a lot of people by surprise when they see me go. Barney's owner flung the ball and I shot off with him. On the first occasion, Barney got there first and picked up the ball. I was a few feet behind. He ran back towards his owner but wouldn't give her the ball. He dropped it a few yards away from her and I saw my window of opportunity. I grabbed the ball and ran and dropped it at my owner's feet. She made an imaginary throw and Barney went off in that direction. He was such a fool. I'd seen her do this before and knew to wait until I really did see the ball go. She threw the ball and off I went to collect it. Somehow Barney had managed to do a triangular run and got there just as I did. But Barney is the perfect gentleman and he let me pick it up. We ran back together to his owner. I wasn't going to give her the ball until she exchanged it for a biscuit. I had already learnt it was quite easy to train people to do this. Just stand there with the ball and when they give you a biscuit, you give them the ball. Anyway, that was how it worked. She threw the ball again and off went Barney.

But then, oh joy of joys, I turned to my right and for the first time in my life saw boys playing football. This was the game that I was born to play. Forget golf. It was football, for real, right there in front of me on the recreation ground.

I ran towards the boys – how could I not do that? There were six of them, just kicking the ball around, and I saw immediately that I could take it from them. As one boy kicked it right across the pitch to another, I seized my opportunity. I ran in, pushed the ball with the end of my nose and shot off at full speed. The boys didn't chase me. They just looked amazed. I put my head down and ran. I just kept going. Oh the feeling of that football on my nose; it was exhilarating. I pushed it with my nose, prodded it with my paws, turning it to the left and turning it to the right. Immediately, I could feel complete nose/paw control.

And then I heard them shouting, 'Come here, dog.' Ahead of me was a ditch and I knew if I let the ball go in there, the game would be over. So I just turned, bringing the football under perfect control, swinging out to the left and then dribbling it forwards. I was bound for Miss Ingrid's School of Correction on Monday and this was probably my last chance of real naughtiness and freedom. Equally, I knew that if I was to be a perfect footballer, I must display good manners and sportsmanship. I must give up the ball, but first I must show

The joy of football – nose/paw co-ordination

my skilful stuff. I ran to the other end of the pitch, with the boys now chasing me, and pushed the ball into the goal. I had scored on my very first outing with a football. I woofed a hoorah-it's-a goal woof!

The biggest boy cheered and claimed the goal for his team. The others didn't like to argue. Barney came up to me, full of congratulations and the boys took back their football.

'It's quite some dog you've got there, missus. Who does he play for?'

'Actually, she's a girl.'

'I've never seen a girl play football like that, missus. They're usually pretty hopeless. She might be the best girl footballer in the country; but that wouldn't take much doing.'

Me, the best girl footballer in the country. Oh my God! Named after the world's best-ever woman golfer and perhaps the best girl footballer. Wow! What news I would have to tell Edward when we got back.

'Come on, Annika. Come on, Barney. I think you've both had quite enough excitement for the day. Time to go home.'

We said our goodbyes and I told Barney I thought he should behave properly and get in the car without a fuss. If not, he might find himself despatched to Miss Ingrid's School of Correction with me.

His owner had learnt quite a lot. She put the key in the ignition, started the car, Barney jumped in, she got out and shut the back door and off they went.

I was in love. I was in love with Barney with his lovely soft ears and his big floppy tail and his lovely brown eyes.

But that wasn't all. I had found the true love of my life. From now on it was football. Perhaps I might even have a football of my own one day.

10

Temptation

It was Saturday. I had slept downstairs in my cage.

'Come on, Annika. We've a busy day ahead of us. We're off to Miss Ingrid's School of Correction tomorrow, so I've got lots of work to do today.'

Even though I was due to go off for three days of strict training, she still took me to my puppy school in Cambridge. I really did enjoy this. The people who ran the puppy classes knew all of us by name and never even bothered with our owners' names. I thought this was a jolly good idea. The puppy training involved teaching us with rewards. Some people had little biscuits, others had special liver cake, but the most popular rewards, with both dogs and owners, was some nice, yellow cheese.

Edward, who as I always say is a very wise cat, used to tell me about Dick Whittington, who became Lord Mayor of London. Edward said Dick Whittington lived hundreds of years ago and he had a cat who was a great, great, and many more greats, grandfather of Edward's. When Dick Whittington and his cat arrived in London, they found that the streets of London were paved with gold.

The streets of Cambridge, or at least the puppy school field, weren't paved with gold. But they were paved with cheese.

I spent most of my time at the classes sniffing out pieces of cheese that other dogs had dropped. We learnt to walk beautifully to heel, always on the left side of our owners. It was pretty obvious how to persuade me to walk close beside her. A biscuit in her pocket or rubbing a little cheese on her left leg (if she was wearing shorts) would get me hugging right in beside her.

We used to walk round in circles, weaving in and out of other dogs, which taught everyone to be quiet and good.

One of the scariest dogs in the class was a German shepherd. Edward had taught me a couple of German phrases. *Guten Tag* – good day – was a polite greeting. *Danke schön*, uttered as I passed him, was a polite thank you. But far more frightening to me was the border collie. He would just stare and stare and never take his eyes off me. I thought Edward could stare for a long time but, in the end, the border collie would always win against me and I would blink or look away. That's how they control sheep.

Anyway, this day we did some weaving in and out, walked to heel and I sniffed up lots of cheese, and then we played the best game of musical chairs. We all walked round in a circle on our leads close to our owners' heels. The instructor would drop her arm, our owners would immediately say 'Sit' and the last dog to sit would be out. Eventually, there would be a winner. The winner didn't get a prize. It was just pride of performance.

A few weeks earlier, when we first played the game, I sat down smartly on command. Mum Maggie had always impressed upon Kiki and Emily and me that show dogs didn't sit, but as I wasn't going to be a show dog, I thought sitting was probably a good idea. After a couple of weeks, though, I couldn't see any point in the game. To me, the real winner was the dog who sat down last in the first round. He or she would be let off the next rounds, and be able to sniff the hedge for interesting smells, pick up more bits of cheese or join the owner for a cup of tea.

So, on this occasion, as soon as the instructor dropped her arm, everyone else in the class sat. I stayed standing just long enough to be sure I would be last, and escape first.

'That's you out, Annika.' Yippee, off to more exciting pastimes.

On the way home, my owner phoned Barney's owner to see if they would like to come round later.

'Of course, we're off to the Lake District tomorrow and Miss Ingrid's School of Correction. But I'm sure Annika and Barney would enjoy playing together this evening. The weather looks good and we'll do a barbecue. See you later.'

I had a fairly lazy afternoon, exhausted after the puppy class. My owner got two lovely big steaks out of the fridge for the barbecue, rubbed them with salt and pepper and nice, smelly oil, and put them on plates on the patio table ready for the barbecue. She laid the table with mats and glasses and brought out a big bowl of salad, some French bread and a few other goodies.

We'd had a barbecue once before but that wasn't a great success because it was only a little portable one and Edward knocked it over and everything was ruined. This time my

Edward – the domesticated cat!

owner got out the big barbecue, filled it with charcoal and lit it.

'That's good, Annika. It should be ready to cook in about thirty minutes. Let's hope our visitors get here before then.'

I heard Barney's car arrive in the drive. He hadn't yet achieved his aim of having a harness and being able to sit in the front seat, and his owner let him out of the back. Edward was there to greet them. I think Edward had met Barney before but probably with a different car. Edward has a ritual of peeing on any new car that arrives at our house. He points his bottom towards one wheel or the front number plate and squirts at it. I think that way he'll always know the visiting vans and cars. If he did get in one and got lost again, he would find the car to bring him back. Anyway, he 'christened' Barney's car.

'I've brought a bottle of wine. Are we having steak? I've brought red. And I've also brought a squeaky ball. I thought Annika might enjoy that.'

'Yes please. I certainly will enjoy another squeaky ball.'

She threw it for me and I siezed my chance to show off. I had one ball in my mouth and could tap the other one along like a little football. It wasn't as good as a football because it was too small, but they could easily see my paw/eye co-ordination. Off I ran round the garden with the ball, while Barney sniffed all the trees and flower beds, like boy dogs do.

And then I spotted a window of opportunity. The owner was, of course, extremely silly to put temptation in my way. I could see the two steaks sitting on the patio table and had already worked out that I could probably reach them by clambering on to one of the wooden armchairs. It was actually quite simple. I wasn't like Edward, who could just jump on to the table, but the combination of a little side table and a wooden armchair made it ridiculously easy.

I thought it best to take just one steak because the owner might not realise it had gone. If I took both, it would be pretty obvious they had been stolen. I dragged the steak carefully off the plate and carefully off the table and on to the ground beneath. It was while I was dragging it across the lawn that I realised I was being watched. Edward was all ready to come after me for his share – floating like a butterfly and stinging like a bee! So I bit off a little bit and dropped it at his feet. Barney took a sniff of the steak but the pepper made him sneeze and he carried on checking out all the trees and bushes. Then he

Too much to carry

cocked his leg, as boy dogs do, on the owner's precious tomato plants, full of tomatoes, in a large patio pot. I wouldn't be eating those again but I assumed that the owner, the gardener and the housekeeper would!

Barney went off to find his owner. Everyone was round the other side of the house but soon my owner arrived to see how the barbecue was going.

'Annika!' she shrieked. 'You wretched creature! You've stolen one of the steaks! Thank goodness we're off to the School of Correction tomorrow. Three days there should sort you out.'

Barney and his owner came round the corner at that moment and I just knew my owner was very, very angry indeed, especially as Barney's owner was prattling on about what a good boy Barney was.

'Of course, Barney is a highly disciplined gundog. Retrievers are so good. That's why they make brilliant gundogs and are used for guide dogs for the blind and various assistance dogs. You can't really beat a golden retriever or a Labrador if you want obedience. One of the problems of choosing something

Best of friends

like a Cardigan corgi is that they probably do have a rebellious streak. I can quite understand why you're taking Annika to Miss Ingrid's School of Correction. I don't suppose they've ever had a golden retriever needing that kind of training.'

She just went on and on and on about perfect Barney, without appreciating that he had cocked his leg on the tomato plants, and she was scoffing tomatoes from that same bush whenever she drew breath between sentences.

'I think the barbecue looks ready to use. Perhaps you could cut the steak in two. I'll just go and get the sausages, beef burgers and chicken.'

With that my owner walked round the side of the house. Once out of sight of her friend, she turned and waved her fist at me, and mouthed 'dash' but I could just hear 'dash – how could you do that, Annika?' She didn't go into our kitchen, though. She shot into the golf-club kitchen next door and collected the extra meat from the chef. She wasn't going to let on to Barney's owner that I was a thief. She was covering up for my crime.

While they cooked and ate their dinner, I could hear my owner telling Barney's owner that I was already an exceptionally well-trained dog, and that the School of Correction was really just to give me the final, finishing touches.

Enjoying her barbecue, Barney's owner suggested, 'Do you think Barney and Annika could have just a tiny morsel of steak? Barney has been such a good boy.'

'No. Annika, has impeccable manners and I certainly wouldn't encourage her to be fed at the table.'

It is just too tempting

Both our owners couldn't stop praising us enough. It became quite competitive between them. But afterwards, Barney wouldn't get in the car. Turn on the ignition and start the car. He'll think you're going without him. That's it. He's jumped in. As Edward said, it was probably the huge blast of carbon monoxide into Barney's face as the car started that prompted him to jump in.

As they backed out, his owner was heard to shout, 'I do hope you and Annika get on well at the School of Correction. I'm sure she'll come back a reformed character. Oh and I do so love those tiny, fresh little tomatoes on your patio. They're the sweetest I've ever tasted. I think I'll plant some in my own garden next year. What did you call them? Tom Thumb? I think Barney would like them, too. Good boy.'

I'm sure I saw Edward wink!

11

Off to School

'Come on, Annika, sleepy head. Rise and shine. We've lots to do today. I think it'll be a five-hour journey to Miss Ingrid's with a stop on the way.'

She packed my bed and some extra bedding, my leads and collars, bottles of water and my bowls. She had arranged for the housekeeper to come to stay to look after Edward and Sophie while we were away. We were soon ready to go.

Goodbye everyone

Can I take Mouse with us please?

She decided it would be a treat for me to sit on the front seat in my smart, blue harness, clipped to the seat belt. It was good to be able to see what she was doing and nice of her to stroke me every now and then and to tell me about the journey. A long car journey like that is quite interesting. The radio was on most of the time for traffic news but, as she explained, being a Sunday, the roads weren't very busy. She also had a man speaking to her all the time, telling her the way. She called him Sidney Satnav. I couldn't figure out where Sidney was but he seemed to know exactly where we were. She spoke to Sidney quite often when he gave her instructions – 'Thank you, Sidney,' or 'No, Sidney. You're out of date. The roundabout's gone.' Sidney seemed to be quite good company but not as good as I am.

Barney's owner phoned during the journey. It cut into the radio programme, which I found quite irritating. I was listening to the football results and wanted to know whether my team, Newcastle, had won. I was just daydreaming that, with my black-and-white coat, I could one day be their mascot and dribble a ball on to the pitch.

After a couple of hours travelling we arrived at Scotch Corner where we filled up with petrol. My owner took me for a little walk, just to stretch my legs, and then I saw it – a sign to Newcastle, home of the world's greatest football team, my team. My owner put me in the back of the car, which was quite a relief, because although I didn't have contact with her, I could at least stretch my legs and walk around. But instead of heading off towards Newcastle we turned the other way, climbing higher and higher on a rather wiggly road.

'Look, Annika. See those red-and-white poles all along the road. That's because in the winter the snow is so deep that they're often the only way of finding the road.' I couldn't see this was of much interest in the middle of summer but I gave her a thank-you-for-the-information woof, just to make her feel I was interested.

'And now, Annika, we're coming into Cumbria. They have red squirrels here. You know the grey squirrels that Edward chases? Well, the red squirrel is much rarer and more important. You can see the signs saying watch out for red squirrels. Everyone knows of grey squirrels but very few people have seen red ones.'

Yes, I thought, it was probably rather like corgis. Everyone knows the Pembroke corgi but even most vets have never seen a Cardigan corgi and most people don't even know we exist.

The owner was conversing quite aggressively with Sidney Satnav. I think we were near the farmhouse where we would be staying but Sidney Satnav was leading us round in circles. Sidney could see the farm but he couldn't seem to lead us to the entrance. My owner decided to stop to phone the house and get directions, but we were so far up into the hills that she couldn't get a signal. We had to drive away a couple miles, back into red-squirrel territory, before she could get reception on her phone.

'Hello, we've found your farm but we can't find the entrance. Oh please don't apologise. Our road doesn't have a name, either. OK, back down the road, past the phone box, look for the milk churn and we'll find you. Yes, that would be great. I'd love a cup of tea when we get there. Oh yes, I'll make sure the dog doesn't chase the sheep. Yes please, and she would also love a bowl of tea. See you in a few minutes.'

'Goodness, Annika, Sidney Satnav might be fine getting us to places but he does tend to let me down at the last moment. Sidney, I'm going to switch you off. Here we are, Annika. Look at the sheep on the left and the cattle on the right. Let's enjoy our little holiday.'

I wasn't sure it was going to be a holiday. I was quite frightened about the School of Correction. It was all right for my owner. She could think of it as a holiday, but I didn't.

'Oh hello, how lovely to meet you. This must be Annika. Isn't she lovely. What on earth is she? A Cardigan corgi. I thought perhaps she was a collie crossed with a dachshund. Aren't her ears absolutely precious! Now do come on in. I'll show you to your room. We get quite a lot of people staying here for Miss Ingrid's School of Correction, so we have special rooms with stone floors, no carpets to get grubby, where dogs are absolutely welcome. Bowls of water on the floor are fine, dogs are welcome to jump on beds and really it's just a home from home. You'll have enough strict behaviour at the school and I'm sure you'll welcome being able to relax and unwind after a hard day at the office. Now, come on into the lounge and let's have tea. Yes, of course Annika can come, too. A pot of tea for you and a bowl full of tea for Annika. Would she like a little sugar in it? Isn't she a sweetie?

'Now, as much as we love dear Miss Ingrid, a lot of people do find her quite intimidating. She's terribly good with dogs and they all seem to adore her. But she has sometimes had the owners in tears. She always takes the view that a poorly behaved dog is the fault of the owner. And she makes that quite clear. Anyway, I've got supper for you and a bowl of lamb and scraps for Annika, if she would like it.'

I went off to our room for the night with quite a spring in my step. After what our hostess had said I was thoroughly looking forward to my training. When it was time to turn the lights out, I clambered on to the bed beside my owner.

'Goodnight, Annika. I'm sure we'll have a good day tomorrow.'

I am so worried about tomorrow

But her voice sounded a little bit shaky and slightly tearful. I gave her a don't-worry-Old-Girl woof. I'm here to look after you at Miss Ingrid's School of Correction.

I was soon fast asleep, dreaming of big bowls of tea, red squirrels, sheep and cattle, and one day going straight on north to Newcastle for football.

12

To Work on an Egg

The sun was just peeping through the curtains and I snuggled up closer to my owner, remembering where we were.

'Morning, Annika.'

I gave a morning-Old-Girl woof, and pushed up even closer for comfort. It might be quite a frightening day. She cuddled me back. I think she was a bit scared, too.

My owner got dressed, put down a bowl of biscuits for me and made her way to the farmhouse kitchen for breakfast. A minute later she was back.

'Our hostess says you should come into breakfast as well, Annika. This really is a dog-friendly place.'

Breakfast was brilliant. I had my own plate with bits of sausage and bacon and toast.

'Tea or coffee?' enquired the hostess.

'Oh, I'll have tea please.'

The hostess shouted back to her husband in the kitchen, 'That's tea for two, dear. Now does Annika like eggs?' My owner said that I had never had an egg and the hostess seemed amazed and horrified. 'We always train our puppies from a very young age with eggs. Let's see if she'll like one.'

The hostess brought in an egg. It looked rather interesting

and worth playing with. The floors of the breakfast room, dining room and lounge were made of large, grey slabs. There wasn't much carpet around, just a nice, soft rug in front of the fire. I thought I would have to discuss this with Edward when I got home. He was sure to know the reason. Perhaps they had a stone floor because they were poor and couldn't afford carpet. Perhaps they had a stone floor so that you could hear what was going on. Every time anyone walked across the room it made a clip-clop sound.

And then the farmer's son walked through in dirty muddy boots and left a trail of mud across the floor. 'I'll brush that up later, Mum.' Perhaps the farmer's wife didn't have a housekeeper with a vacuum cleaner or perhaps she couldn't use a vacuum cleaner, like my owner couldn't. Perhaps it was to keep the floor clean.

Anyway, I would ask Edward when I got home. I wondered if they had a cat. Then out of the corner of my eye I saw a lovely, striped black and grey cat sitting on the top of what my owner later said was a piano. The hostess introduced him to us as Tom, said he was perfectly friendly and did a thoroughly good job of keeping mice away. Tom was given a small piece of sausage, which he accidently knocked off the piano on to the floor. I was just about to go and get it for myself when Tom jumped down, as silently as cats do, arched his back, puffed out his body and tail, stared at me with huge yellow eyes and ate the piece of sausage. He jumped back on to the middle layer of the piano and, as he landed, it made a loud, musical noise. He walked the length of the piano, making music as

Always carry something – be useful

he went. From there he leapt up on to the top of the piano, curled himself round and round, like Edward does, getting his tail and his paws in just the right position before standing to attention. He was just like a statue.

Anyway, now to my egg. The hostess put the egg on the floor and I nudged it along with my nose. It didn't run in perfectly straight lines like a ball but wobbled from side to side. The combination of its funny shape and the roughness of the stone floor meant that it was fun and quite unpredictable. I pushed it along. The silly thing didn't talk like a squeaky ball. It didn't roll very truly and I couldn't really see the point of it. I patted it gently with my paw, nudged it with my nose but wasn't particularly impressed. Then I thought I would pick it up in my mouth and take it back to my owner's feet. I kept the egg in my mouth and couldn't figure out what I was supposed to do.

'Do you think Annika would like to go out in the garden with her egg? She has a lovely soft mouth and that's what we always look for in the puppies. Ingrid always trains the gundogs with eggs and I'm sure she'll be mighty impressed with Annika. Come on, Annika, out in the garden for a few minutes with that egg and let's see what you make of it.'

Well, I wandered out into the little garden where there was an area of grass all fenced off away from the farm fields. Beyond the fence were the sheep and the cattle and horses but really I couldn't be bothered with them. What was I supposed to do with this egg? I carried it around, put it on the grass. Carried it some more and then put it down. Really, who was interested in a boring old egg?

What do I do with this egg?

And then the back door opened, the hostess shouted to me to come in and bring the egg. I gave the silly egg to my owner who tapped it on the side of my bowl. Soon the egg wasn't an egg any more. It had turned into a shiny, clear liquid with a big yellow blob in the middle. I hesitated for about half a second and then stuck my tongue into this beautiful, creamy drink. The hostess added a drop of creamy milk. Oh, wow! Now I knew what an egg was for.

We jumped in the car – me in the front, wearing my blue harness, attached to the seat belt. The hostess spoke to my owner as she shut the farm gate behind us. She wouldn't be doing meals at the house that evening but suggested a lovely pub, whatever a pub was, in Appleby.

And so we set off, both a bit fearful, to Miss Ingrid's School of Correction. The hostess was waving and shouting, 'Good luck!'

13

The School of Correction

We drove the short distance to the school and Miss Ingrid was there to greet us. Before she had even really welcomed us or exchanged the time of day she made it clear she disapproved of dogs sitting in harnesses on the front seat next to their owners. She thought it far better for a dog to travel in the back in its own cage.

'Shall I bring Annika in on her lead?'

'No,' said Miss Ingrid. 'We'll leave her in the car. Please put her in her cage in the back. I always start with owners. A badly behaved owner produces a badly behaved dog. Conversely, a badly behaved dog, in all but the most unusual circumstances, is the result of a badly disciplined owner.'

My owner was gone for quite a considerable time while I sat patiently in the back of the car. When they both came out to fetch me, my owner looked a little flustered. She had brought a couple of leads for me. There was a nice red and green one showing pictures of dogs and bones. Then there was my very special lead, a long string one that shot out at various lengths and allowed me a bit of freedom to walk ahead of her.

'I always confiscate those dreadful extending leads straight away. You'll never get a well-behaved, controlled dog using that. They're the scourge of dog trainers. I have a whole cupboard full of confiscated retractable leads. Yes, you can keep it, provided you promise never to use it again. Please put her on the other lead and we'll get started.'

We went into Miss Ingrid's classroom and I curled up on the floor on the rug, with just one ear on the conversation.

'Would you like a mug of tea?'

My owner said she would and could she please have two spoonfuls of sugar. I thought this was unusual because she didn't take sugar. And then I remembered some advice I'd heard on the radio – give tea with sugar to someone suffering from shock or distress. That's why she wanted sugar with her tea. She was in shock. I felt a little bit sorry for my owner.

They talked a lot about my behaviour and my owner's life with me. My owner explained that the real problem was that I often ran away and simply wouldn't come back when called. She explained that we lived in the middle of a golf course, so getting out on to roads was not a problem, but in theory I could walk for miles and get lost. My owner explained that she wanted me to sit still reliably and not chase golf balls. Miss Ingrid raised one eyebrow at the mention of golf balls.

'Have you ever had problems with her with sheep? That's the real killer – a dog that chases sheep. As you know, a farmer is entitled to shoot and kill a dog worrying sheep and lambs. That's what a lot of the training here is about. I can usually train any dog to do anything the owner wants, within reason, providing the owner is sensible.

'I've never worked with a Cardigan corgi before but I can see straight away that she has fantastic hearing with those

Here I am

enormous ears. That's the problem with some collies. They don't always hear as well as one would imagine. Annika also has great eye contact. She wants to learn and she's looking for guidance. I think the only dogs that really aren't good to train are Jack Russells because they have such an inbuilt instinct to chase rats, but I'm sure Annika will respond.

'People have definite ideas about what is and isn't an easy dog to train. I don't know if you know of anyone with a golden retriever. We have to do more work here with golden retrievers and Labradors than with any other breed.'

I immediately thought of Barney and his owner and her words of wisdom that a golden retriever would never have to go to Miss Ingrid's School of Correction. I tried to wink at my owner with this message. I knew she must be thinking the same but didn't dare chuckle.

'People see golden retrievers and Labradors as being perfect as guide dogs. They *are* perfect in that situation. But then, of course, they're bred to be guide dogs, brought up to it from a very early age and then have two years very strict training. The golden retrievers and Labradors we see here are nearly always gundogs or pet dogs who won't retrieve properly. The key thing about a gundog, and particularly the retriever, is that it must bring what it retrieves right back to the handler's hands. It's no good bringing a fluttering, injured pheasant almost back to the handler, dropping it on the ground and letting it escape. They can also be gun shy, and a bit wimpish. I get owners who simply cannot get a golden retriever or Labrador to get into the back of a car. Often it's simply because they haven't had enough exercise and don't want to go home. All I can say is thank goodness you haven't brought me another golden retriever.

'Now, let's see if there really is a problem with Annika running away.'

So we headed off out of her farmhouse and on to the land next door. We walked a little way together with me on the lead and then she let me go. I know I should have stayed with them but the temptation was just too great. I ran off, bounding up the hillside, sniffing at the green grass and brown shoots of marshy grass. It was all so different. There wasn't just fox poop or duck poop to roll in but big dollops of what I discovered to be sheep poop and horse poop. Fling a bit here, roll in a bit there. It was great to be free. I could hear Miss Ingrid and my owner calling my name. Why would I want to go back and lose this new-found freedom? I turned just to acknowledge I knew they were there, and continued to bound along.

Thank goodness it's not another retriever!

Eventually, I came to a stone wall. I couldn't see any way through it and I couldn't see any way over it. I ran to the left along the wall; no way out there. I ran to the right along the stone wall; same again. By this time, Miss Ingrid and my owner were nearly upon me and I decided it was time to play the evade-capture game. It was such fun. Miss Ingrid went one way; my owner went the other. Edward's words of wisdom had come back to me. 'You must never let them get you in a corner.' I realised what he meant. If I went to the corner of the wall, they could creep up on me and, since there was no way of escape, they would surely catch me. I moved right back to the middle of the wall. I must think this out quite carefully. I had my back to the wall but with a stream a couple of yards to my left. Ha, ha! I think I've got you beat.

Miss Ingrid and my owner continued to walk up towards me and Miss Ingrid was calling, 'Annika.' Just as they reached me, I shot through the stream and they couldn't follow. In fact, I now noticed that Miss Ingrid was wearing very big rubber boots and she did follow me, but I was off with a mind of my own. I was not going to be corrected. I wanted my freedom. I could hear my owner wittering that this was the problem with me. But joy of joys, I could hear Miss Ingrid shouting back that this was only natural. She made me feel sensible and perfectly reasonable and my owner a little bit stupid. I began to feel sorry for my owner but I wasn't going to give in.

Miss Ingrid told my owner that they would go back to the house. I was perfectly safe out here and would return eventually. She waded back through the stream and walked towards the farmhouse with my owner. Since my hearing is so good, I could hear her telling my owner not to look back. Off they went. It must have been a very difficult decision for my owner to leave me out there.

I found duck muck to roll in, nice and smelly, flung some sheep poop into the air and did some more sniffing. I chased a rabbit but it shot down a hole. I chased another rabbit and it shot through some wire netting. I couldn't follow and was afraid to put my head through in case I got stuck. I chased a red squirrel but it shot up a tree. I sat at the bottom of the tree for a minute or so shouting at it but it wasn't going to come down the tree to play with me. I found a few hummocks of earth that had been newly turned over and I could hear something scurrying around under one mound. Earth was being flicked into the air. I dug at the mound with my paws and a little, black, silky creature emerged.

'Good morning, Dog. I'm a mole; this is my hole. Please leave me alone.' I tried to ask Mr Mole what he was doing but he just went back underground.

By now I was feeling lonely and very bored, and I thought my owner and Miss Ingrid would be back in the warm kitchen, probably with another cup of tea. I found my way to the back door of the farmhouse, sat outside and woofed. I did a hello-I'm-back-to-see-you woof. That was followed by an I'm-bored-and-lonely woof. Third was a please-could-you-let-me-in woof but still they didn't open the door. So I decided to

I better go back

woof even louder. The next one was a help-I-am-really-really-frightened woof. The back door opened and there was Miss Ingrid.

'Oh, Annika. You've decided to come back at last,' she said. She was still wearing her rubber boots and she took me out into the yard, hosed off all the duck muck, dried me down quite roughly with a towel and then took me back into the kitchen.

'We'll try that exercise once more, Annika. You can stay here,' she said to my owner. 'I'll see whether Annika will respond to me.'

Off we went into the field, me entrapped on the lead. Then she let me go and off I ran. Again, the terrible temptation was too hard to resist, what with the thought of seeing Mr Mole, chasing the red squirrel, flinging some sheep poop and rolling in gorgeous duck muck. Miss Ingrid gave two blasts on a whistle, which were really ear-splitting, and turned back to the kitchen. I'd had a couple of minutes of freedom but I thought it was best to return with her. By the time I got back to the kitchen door it was firmly shut. I gave my please-let-me-in woof, my here-I-am woof, and then my I-am-very-sorry woof. The door opened and in I went.

'Oh, Annika. You *are* a good girl. I'm so pleased. She really is good.' My owner was delighted.

'Now please don't witter at the poor dog. She doesn't understand a word you say and we have to get clear, definite commands. One of the problems is people who try to carry on conversations with their dogs,' said Miss Ingrid. 'You need to understand that a dog does not understand what you say. They go on sounds and definite commands. I had a woman here last week who had an uncontrollable Labrador puppy. She was all namby-pamby with it and probably read it bedtime stories. The husband let slip just how stupid this woman was. I really couldn't believe it. He said that she would not only carry on a conversation with the dog, as if it would understand, but she would also talk to the satnav in her car. The husband said that she called it Samuel Satnav and would try to get Samuel to answer back. Now when you get someone as ludicrous as that, trying to carry on a conversation with a satnav, doesn't it tell you why they have a dog that's totally confused?'

I looked at my owner and she looked down at me. I remembered Mum's words of wisdom about cocking your head on one side so that your owner knows you understand. I thought it best at this point not to let on that I knew about my owner talking to Sidney Satnav. So I pretended I didn't understand. I thought those were the best tactics.

Well, then the training started.

I was given a metal choke chain and Miss Ingrid explained to my owner just how to fit it. And then she attached a very, very long green lead. The lead was about eight paces long. Miss Ingrid put a black whistle on a red string around her neck and gave my owner an identical one. It was a very hard exercise indeed. I walked to heel beside Miss Ingrid and she shouted, 'Sit.' I sat. 'Walk on.' She gave a little tug to the chain and set off with her left foot. 'Sit.' And I sat. 'Walk on.' And I walked on. We did more and more. She left me sitting there, walked away to the end of the rope lead, shouted, 'Come,' gave a little pull on the lead and I ran towards her. 'Sit.' And I sat. Somehow, I just wanted to do what she said. She wasn't particularly kind. She wasn't going to give me biscuits. She wasn't going to punish me if I did anything wrongly. Somehow, I was mesmerised and knew I had to do what she said. 'Oh Miss Ingrid, I so want to be a good girl for you.'

First lessons

When my owner tried exactly the same thing, I didn't really feel I needed to obey. She said, 'Sit,' 'Come,' 'Stay,' in such a sweet, gentle way that my ears were much more interested in the noise of the sheep and the cattle in the next-door fields. My concentration wasn't on her at all.

I could hear Miss Ingrid shouting at her, 'For goodness sake, tell the dog firmly what you want. Don't confuse the poor creature. Now come on, dear, tell her how it is. And pull her on the chain. Just a little tug is all she needs. You aren't going to pull her head off, dear. She's still controlling you.'

I could feel that my owner didn't really like being called dear. It had made her sound weak and feeble. My owner teaches golf and is very, very direct to her pupils. Why on earth was she like this with me?

Anyway, we finished our day's training. Miss Ingrid seemed thrilled to bits with my performance and gave my owner homework to look at before the next day's training. My owner put me in the back of the car and we headed off to Appleby for supper. The farmer's wife, our hostess, had given her the postcode for Sidney Satnav and he spoke directions. 'Turn right in three hundred yards and follow River Lane.'

'Which way, Sidney, which way?' My owner chuckled and then she started talking to me but stopped mid-sentence and thought better of it.

I would have so much to tell Edward when we returned home, and I could tell Barney that golden retrievers aren't all as perfect as his owner thinks.

14

Yes, I'm Annika

We parked in Appleby, which seemed a really nice little town. My owner left me in the car and I could see her heading towards the pet shop up a little lane. A moment later she came out, returned to the car, put me on my lead (not the forbidden extending lead) and took me off to the pet shop, too.

Well, I have never smelt such gorgeous things – pigs' ears, chewy bones and all manner of delicious goodies just at nose height for a Cardigan corgi. While the owner was paying for a couple of chewy bones, which had been put into a small brown paperbag, I put my nose in a basket of squeaky balls. I squeaked them, and squeaked them and squeaked them some more. The shopkeeper laughed and asked whether I was good with a ball. My owner said I was and then, joy of joys, asked him whether by any chance he had a football suitable for a little dog. I dragged her over to the corner of the shop. There they were – red and white, and black and white. But the shopkeeper, who obviously knew the habits of dogs inside out, said that really the best thing, instead of a football, was a small basketball. He explained that dogs with sharp teeth can puncture a football very easily but that basketballs, as well as being smaller and heavier, are more robust. The basketball

My new football

was orange. My owner decided to buy the basketball but I kept woofing with a please-buy-me-a-football woof. So she bought me the black-and-white football as well. And then, to be totally fair, she asked the shopkeeper if he had any suitable presents for cats. He produced a furry, grey, battery-operated, wind-up mouse, which scurried along the counter. I didn't think Edward would be very impressed with that but it was a token. And then he had some special cat toys that bounced up and down on elastic strings and I thought that one of those hanging on the banisters of the stairs would be just right for Sophie. I gave a little woof of approval and the shopkeeper added that to the carrier bag.

My owner asked whether there was anywhere good to eat nearby and the shopkeeper suggested the pub our hostess had mentioned. It was just next door.

'It's a long time since we've seen a lovely Cardigan corgi in Appleby and I know they'll welcome you there,' he said.

I was in raptures. He recognised me as a Cardigan corgi. He didn't think I was part collie and part dachshund. He didn't make the usual joke about whether I was a cross between a donkey and a sausage dog. Here was somebody who knew about Cardigan corgis. I was going to like Appleby.

We went into the pub next door, which had a stone floor, big pine tables and a roaring fire on the other side of the room. My owner asked whether it was possible for the dog to come in as well. The woman behind the bar opened her eyes wide.

'Oh my goodness, Harry,' she shouted towards the kitchen. 'It's a lovely Cardigan corgi.' Smiling at us, she said, 'Yes, of course you can come in, my dear. We welcome lovely, well-behaved dogs, and put up with their owners, too! Would you like to sit over by the fire? I'll bring you the menu and I'm sure chef can find something for the dog. What's her name?'

'Annika,' said my owner.

A man in the corner looked up from his newspaper and muttered, 'I suppose she's named after that wretched woman golfer, Annika Sorenstam. Ridiculous woman went round the golf course in 59 the other week. Set a new world record and made us all feel like blithering idiots.'

My owner was just about to explain that I was called Annika because my parents were Finnish – at least, I think that's what she was going to say – but another man took up the conversation.

'You don't see many Cardigan corgis. I think they're probably the best farm dog there is but nobody much knows about them. I've got a cousin in Wales who has a Cardigan and swears by it. Says they're much better than collies. A collie is fine with sheep but they need one hell of a lot of training. He says the Cardigan corgi he has is brilliant. It's only a young one, not quite a year old, but it drives the herd of cattle from one field to another, straight along the farm road, never lets any of them go, and he's thinking about giving it real training to work with sheep. He's not sure whether the sheep will respond to being pushed from behind rather than being stared at, like a collie does, but he'll try him out.

'I wish there were more Cardigan corgis around. How old is this one?'

'Oh, she's coming up to one year.'

'Well, that's a great age for training. Yes, my cousin is really delighted with his Cardigan corgi. It's called Bryn and came from a Mrs Cole in Birmingham.'

I couldn't believe what I was hearing. They were talking about my lovely brother, Bryn. Yes, he had gone to a farm and it was good to hear how well he was doing. Oh my goodness! If I ever met up with Mum Maggie again or Emily or Toby, I could tell them all about Bryn and his successes.

Everyone was surprised to hear that I came from Mrs Cole, too, and my owner explained that I certainly wasn't for sale. There were a few issues with me, particularly getting me to return, and we were having training at Miss Ingrid's School of Correction.

My brother Bryn

'Oh,' said the farmer, 'our Miss Ingrid's quite a girl, you know. There's nobody better in this part of the country for teaching owners how to train their dogs. The dogs all seem to adore her but not so sure about the owners.'

My owner nodded and ordered steak and kidney pie and a special dog's supper for me. I sat under the table and listened. The man at the bar bought her a glass of red wine. And then the farmer bought her another one and the man who'd sworn about Annika Sorenstam insisted on buying her another one when he discovered she taught golf. It all turned into quite a jolly evening, although I did begin to

Trying to be perfect

get a bit bored. I couldn't open the plastic carrier bag that contained the football, basketball, the presents for Edward and Sophie and a squeaky ball. But somehow the little brown paperbag that contained two chews and a pig's ear sort of fell apart while I wasn't really looking. I thought it best to tidy them up. By the time we left there was nothing left of the brown paperbag or its contents. Fortunately, my owner, having had three large glasses of wine, had forgotten about the brown paperbag, took the carrier bag and nearly forgot to take me. This taught me another good lesson in life. If you're going to commit a misdemeanour, complete the job and cover your tracks.

We set off back up the hill in the car. My owner had forgotten Miss Ingrid's words of advice and I sat on the front seat in my harness. She set Sidney Satnav to direct us back to the farm.

'Turn right in four hundred yards.'

'Look, Sidney, we've got to be really careful. I'm well over the limit and mustn't get caught, so just take it steadily, Sidney, and don't get us lost.'

We found the way back to the farm all right. I did a final wee in the back garden. My owner went in and ordered breakfast for us both for eight o'clock the next morning and off we went to the bedroom. I could see Tom, the cat, prowling up and down on our window sill, opening and closing his mouth and making silent, squeaking noises, like cats do. Why do they do that? They open their mouths as though they're going to squeak and nothing comes out. Still, that's cats for you. I must ask Edward when we get home.

15

Sandy from Skye

'Goodnight, Annika. Thanks for being such a very good girl.' I did a little goodnight-Old-Girl woof, snuggled up beside her on the bed and dreamt of the next day's training with Miss Ingrid.

Breakfast followed much the same pattern. The farmer's wife gave me an egg to take out into the garden while the breakfast was being prepared. I walked around with it, nudged it, pushed it with my paws and again the silly thing just wouldn't walk in a straight line. My owner called me and I returned to the breakfast room, the egg in my mouth. Tom the cat was sitting on the piano and I took the egg over and put it on the carpet below him. He gave me one of those sideways looks that cats give, flicked his tail and produced a kind of good-morning hiss.

My owner picked up the egg, tapped it on the side of the bowl and emptied it in with the rest of my breakfast.

'Would you like a meal here tonight? We're having roast lamb and I've got some other visitors coming as well. They've got a dog, a Skye terrier. I'm sure you'll all get on well.'

My owner agreed that it would be a good idea and we would enjoy the meal. I remembered what Edward had said about being a foreign secretary heavily into home rule for Scotland.

Skye terriers would need special papers to come into England. But as Edward wasn't prime minister, or foreign secretary, I assumed Skye terriers could come and go quite freely across the border. I wondered if, by any chance, he knew my brother Toby, who had gone to Scotland to work on a farm. That would be a bit too much of a coincidence.

We set off to Miss Ingrid's for another day's training. She asked my owner if she had read all her homework. My owner said she had. This wasn't true. My owner had spent so much time in the pet shop and in the pub, drinking red wine, that she had forgotten all about her homework.

So I knew that I must cover her tracks and respond really well. It was down to me to save my owner's embarrassment. I didn't want her to get a ticking off. She had, after all, bought me a football and a basketball, and I would have had a pig's ear and a couple of chews to take home if I hadn't chewed them up in the pub without her knowing.

Today we worked on so many exciting things. I worked on my choke chain with a rope lead ten paces long. I walked and sat, I walked on command. I learnt that one whistle meant 'sit' and two whistles meant 'come'. I sat at the end of the rope. Miss Ingrid gave two sharp whistles, pulled on the rope and I ran right to her feet and sat down. I decided I must respond just as well for my owner. I did want to please her.

And then we did something more advanced. I sat and I stayed. Miss Ingrid commanded me to stay and then walked away from me, right foot first. She walked right to the very end of the rope and then she laid the rope on the ground. My ears were all of a quiver. I wondered what was going to happen. Was I going to run to the end of the lead? No, this time she continued to make me stay and walked in a big circle right around me. As she walked in a circle, I followed her round with my head until my head literally wouldn't turn any further. I had to turn my head to the other side to spot her coming round in a circle to the end of the rope. All the time I stayed sitting. And then when she got back to the end of the rope, she gave two blasts on the whistle and I ran towards her and sat at her feet.

'Yes, this dog is absolutely perfect to train. It's you, my dear. You just have to be firm with her and learn a method. It's hours and hours of practice for several weeks and you'll get there. It's all in my notes. Now, come on, let's see you do it.'

My owner made me sit down. One whistle and I was sitting. She started to walk away from me.

'No,' shouted Miss Ingrid. 'You set off with your left foot when you want the dog to walk with you and you set off with your right foot when you want her to stay. Now come on, do it again. How is the poor dog going to get this right if you can't?'

My owner started again at my side. I stayed sitting and she set off with her right foot, walking to the end of the rope. Then she commanded me to sit and stay. I sat and stayed. I could hear the sheep in the field next door and when I glanced at them, I saw the red squirrel out of the corner of my eye. Temptation was just too great. I shot off towards the squirrel, trailing the lead behind me. But Miss Ingrid was quick off the mark and put her big, booted foot on the end of the rope. Gosh, it tugged at me. Two sharp whistles. Back I went. One whistle, and I sat in my starting place.

The owner tried it again. I felt I had to be reliable and not let her down. For some reason I wanted so much to do what Miss Ingrid wanted me to do but my owner was a soft touch and it wasn't quite the same. Come on, Annika. Pull yourself together and do it properly. My owner commanded me to sit and blew the whistle and walked away, leading with her right foot as she was told. She got to the end of the rope ten paces away. She commanded me to stay and she walked round me in a circle. I didn't bother to watch her because I knew she would come round the other side. My eyes were still on that squirrel. And then I heard a little voice in my head telling me how successful brother Bryn was in Wales. I couldn't let the side down. I swung my head round and watched my owner return to the end of the rope. She went to pick it up to pull me towards her but Miss Ingrid told her to give two sharp blasts on the whistle and see what happened.

I shot towards my owner like a thing possessed and sat bolt upright in front of her. I can do it, Old Girl. I can be a perfect dog if you can be a perfect owner.

We did more training, up and down and up and down. Walk on with the left foot. Sit and walk away with the right foot. I was beginning to get the hang of it, probably much more quickly than my owner. I noticed that Miss Ingrid hardly talked at all while we were outside. She waited until we were back inside for tea break and then she and my owner had lots of talk about writing books and teaching people to do things.

Miss Ingrid couldn't really understand how my owner was such a successful golf coach, teaching all manner of people to play a difficult game like golf, when she seemed so bad and indecisive with me.

After tea break we went for a long walk. I was still on my trailing lead. If I went too far away or failed to listen to the whistle, Miss Ingrid's booted foot would find the end of that rope and bring me back to attention.

'You have to teach the dog the difference between play time and work time. Whenever she has a collar and lead on, it's work time, and whenever it's play time, you take them off. That way she'll understand the difference.'

After a long, tiring day we returned to the farm. That evening, before supper, my owner did do her homework and read Miss Ingrid's notes. I could hear her talking to herself, practising the commands and the whistles.

At supper I met the Skye terrier. 'You may think that you're a very unusual breed of dog and no one much knows who you are, but take it from me, we Skye terriers are even more unusual. There are so few of us that we all know each other. My name's Sandy. That's my pet name. I was named after Sandy Lyle, who is one of Scotland's greatest ever golfers. But I don't expect a wee lass like you would know anything about golf. Ho ho!'

'Actually, it's funny you should say that. My name's Annika, like Annika Sorenstam, the greatest woman golfer who has ever lived. She's Swedish. She set a new world record of 59 a few weeks ago and many men are very cross about that.'

My new friend Sandy, the Skye terrier

'Well there's a thing! A golfing Cardigan corgi! I play golf with my owner at a very smart golf club near Edinburgh, which is men only. Girls are never allowed on the golf course. Once one of the men members had a heart attack and a woman doctor turned up in the ambulance to save him. It was touch and go whether they let her in to treat him or preferred to let him die rather than let a woman on site. Golf at some places in Scotland is a bit odd. The only girls who ever get on our golf course are the owners' girl dogs. In fact, you'd have a lot more chance of getting on the golf course, Annika, than Annika Sorenstam.'

I thought that if Edward had his way and became prime minister and I became minister for sport, I would certainly stop that.

Next morning after breakfast – a bowl of tea, sausage and bacon and my egg – we set off for Miss Ingrid's. On the last day of my correction course we were taken right up to the top of the hillside where we could see for miles and miles. I could see men jumping off the top of hills attached to big orange and yellow birds and flying slowly to the ground. Miss Ingrid referred to them as kites. My owner has a friend who is a keen birdwatcher. She's always talking about watching for red kites and I assumed this is what she meant.

There were sheep everywhere – thousands and thousands of sheep; everywhere I looked, blobs of white, woolly sheep. Some had black faces and a few were brown, or even black,

Sheep and red kites

all over. Edward had once said that I was probably the black sheep of the family. I didn't think black sheep really existed, but here they were. Miss Ingrid was determined that I should learn never to chase sheep. They seemed to move rather slowly and lethargically and I didn't think they looked very interesting at all until one started running and several started running behind her. I wanted to run with them but Miss Ingrid gave a loud blast on the whistle and shouted, 'Sit,' and I sat.

Some sheepdogs, collies, did really clever things with the sheep. I could see them working in pairs, rounding up the sheep and pushing them in certain directions. The sheep seemed rather silly creatures. The obvious thing, if you wanted to defeat the sheepdog, would be to divide into groups and scatter in different directions. Occasionally, one would break

If collies can do it so can I

I think I could do herding, one day!

away and one of the dogs would soon fetch it back. I noticed a man with them, and a van. Miss Ingrid explained to my owner something about the skill of these border collies. She had had young border collies that had occasionally got lost out on the Fells. There were thousands of acres of land with no fences or walls to divide the sheep. The sheep passed their skills on from one generation to the next. Mother taught her daughter, daughter taught her daughter, so that the sheep instinctively knew where they lived.

The job for the morning was to make sure I wouldn't follow sheep, particularly when they had lambs. Sometimes Miss Ingrid had to use collars that gave little electric tickings if the dog ever chased the sheep. I certainly wasn't going to have that. I made sure she was quite satisfied that I would be a good girl and sheep weren't of interest.

The owner had brought a golf club and a few golf balls with her to see if Miss Ingrid could train me not to run after the ball. We worked out a routine. I would sit opposite my owner. She would get ready to hit the golf ball, give one loud blast on the whistle, hold up her hand and say, 'Leave.' She would hit the ball, hope that I was still sitting absolutely stationary and then she would praise me. We did it over and over again, with my owner hitting progressively longer shots while still managing to keep me from moving.

And then all of a sudden temptation just came over me. She did all the right things and then hit the ball much farther than she had hit the other shots. I ran and ran after it. I just couldn't resist it. And then I heard a loud blast on the whistle. Was it the owner or was it Miss Ingrid? I stood absolutely still. I didn't shake my tail. I didn't twitch my ears. I just stood there. I turned round and there they were, my owner and Miss Ingrid both bending over with their hands in front of them, giving two quick blasts of the whistle. I knew what I had to do. I ran back, forgetting all about the golf ball, and arrived at their feet. My owner was all ready to reward me with a biscuit, but was chastised for even thinking of it. 'Remember, it's pride of performance.' And so it was. I felt so puffed up with success that I couldn't wait to get back home to tell Edward and Sophie and Barney what I had achieved. Miss Ingrid and my owner were still marvelling at the workings of the border collie and I felt a little bit deflated. Look what these clever boys and girls were doing. All I had managed to do was to avoid touching a golf ball.

And then it was my moment. Two huge RAF jet planes shot across the sky from right to left, low enough to have tickled the tops of the trees if there had been any.

'My God, I wish they wouldn't fly so damned low,' said Miss Ingrid. 'Look what it's done to those dogs. People lose horses and foals because of these RAF pilots joyriding over the Fells.'

I looked into the valleys below me and the hills to the side of me. The border collies had all just scattered, letting their sheep break up from their well-organised groups. It was a disaster. They were out of control and nowhere to be seen.

And then two more jet planes appeared, away in the sky over to my right. I could hear them before they arrived and I knew what I must do. I must save the day. First, I just sat there. I didn't move. I didn't even twitch my ears. But I wasn't going to have any of this. As the planes approached from my right I plucked up courage, pulled myself to my full height and woofed them on their way. First, it was a loud and stern go-away woof. Then I moved a few paces to follow them and woofed a very definite clear-off woof. And as I woofed again, the planes crossed the sky in front of me and vanished away to my left.

'That's taught you to mess with our sky,' I woofed. 'That's seen them off.'

The collies started to gather their wandering sheep. I had saved the day.

There, you see, a well-trained border collie may be able to control sheep on the Fells but a talented Cardigan corgi can control RAF aeroplanes and teach them a lesson or two!

16

My First Show

We returned from Miss Ingrid's School of Correction both reformed characters. I noticed my owner hardly spoke to Sidney Satnav on the way home. I was determined to behave. Halfway back we stopped at the same service station. There was the sign to the A1 North and Newcastle, where I hoped one day to watch, or even play, football. My owner forgot the rules about having me in the back and put me in my little blue harness in the front of the car for the journey home.

I had so much to tell Edward. In fact, I had so much to tell Barney, but I'm sure my owner wouldn't dare tell Barney's owner how frequently golden retrievers had to go to the School of Correction.

Over the next three weeks my owner religiously did the drills Miss Ingrid had shown her. We walked up and down the length of the garden. And then we walked in an open space in the fields. We did 'sit' and 'stay'. One whistle and I sat. Two whistles and I would come. The good thing about my owner is that she was a golfing champion. She wasn't quite as important as the real Annika but apparently had some modest ability! It meant she was disciplined and very strict with herself and this was just like practising golf.

I wouldn't say I became perfect. I could still be tempted by a squirrel, and on a walk I might get a little farther ahead of the owner than I should. But I sat absolutely still at one blast of the whistle and returned reliably with two blasts of the whistle. This gave me freedom. My owner had the confidence to let me wander freely. The more reliable my returning, the freer I was to explore. My choke chain and the long trailing lead were soon replaced with nice, soft, rope, gundog leads, which can give that little pull on the neck when needed but don't grab like a metal choke chain.

Meanwhile, and just three days after we returned from Cumbria, my owner decided that she and I should have a real bonding treat by going to a companion dog show thirty miles or so from home. I had never been to a dog show and nor had she, but friends had suggested that they would be fun. This one wasn't a big show like Crufts with classes just for pedigree dogs. It did have some classes for pedigree dogs but it also had fun classes for the best ears, the waggiest tail and things like that.

That day changed my life, and my owner's life, too. We arrived at the show and it looked really good fun. It was held on a small sports field by a village hall and there were two rings. The left one was for pedigree dogs, which was where I had to go, and the right one for non-pedigree. Dogs paraded inside the rings, and waiting dogs and their owners sat outside. Most people had brought seats or blankets to sit on, and even little tents to shelter from the sun – it was a very hot day. My owner entered me for just about everything I was eligible to

My first dog show! I am very nervous!

enter. My first class was for the Pedigree Puppy. At least forty of us assembled, in all shapes and sizes. The little ones had to go at the front and the big ones at the back. I was the last of the small dogs and soon cottoned on that we were going to have to be lifted on to a table for the judge to examine.

The only time I had stood on a table before was when I stole the steak at the barbecue. But I watched the others carefully and reckoned I could do the same. Behind me was the start of the big dogs. Right behind me was an enormous Newfoundland. He was a real giant; if he was still a puppy, whatever was he going to grow into? He was definitely one that Edward, as foreign secretary, wouldn't let into the country. All the time that we were waiting he sniffed at my tail, which I thought was

Getting ready for the show!

rather rude. My owner did suggest to his owner that he stand a little bit farther away from me, but she just said that we were all puppies and he wouldn't bite. He didn't bite but I was glad when my owner eventually plonked me on the table and we got out of his way. The judge looked at me closely, and opened my mouth. I had learnt to cope with this at puppy school so wasn't alarmed. Lots of the puppies objected but I felt proud that I didn't. Then I had to walk to one corner of the ring and back again and in a little triangle. My owner and I had both been watching all the puppies before and didn't make too much of a hash of it.

I did laugh at the sniffing Newfoundland. He walked up to the judge, and the judge tried to open his mouth. The Newfoundland growled very noisily, tried to bite him and he and his owner were sent out of the ring. Anyway, after the individual examinations, we all walked round the ring and now I had a nice friendly border collie behind me, who had far better manners. The judge looked at us all and took six of us forwards. I didn't know whether we were being kept in for bad behaviour or had done something good. Eventually, I didn't get a prize or a rosette but the judge said, 'Well done,' and other people smiled as we walked out of the ring.

Then we started on all the fun classes. There was a class for the dog with the nicest ears and I thought I had a good chance in that until I saw a dog with ears so long that they practically brushed the ground. And there was another one with stick-up ears even longer than mine. Again, we were called forward into a line-up of six. Again, I didn't win a prize or a rosette. The same thing happened with nearly every class. The blackest nose, the waggiest tail, the prettiest bitch and the dog and owner most alike. Fortunately, my owner was wearing black shorts, a white shirt and white tennis shoes, so at least she had the uniform right.

I was beginning to feel a little crestfallen because we seemed to come so close to winning and the judges all liked us, but it was only our first go. And then came the moment that changed our lives.

'Hello,' said a rather elderly man. 'I really thought your lovely Cardigan corgi might win best puppy. She's an absolute poppet. Are you going to show her seriously?' And he asked my owner all about me. He asked if he could have a look at me, and as there wasn't a spare table, my owner took me to the back of the car and I stood there while he examined me. He spoke beautifully, softly, and described exactly what a Cardigan corgi should look like. He said, 'breed standard' and then recited all about my feet, my tail and exactly how I should look.

'Where did you get her?' My owner explained that I had come from Mrs Cole.

'Oh good Lord, she isn't one of Maggie's puppies, is she?' I just glowed with pride that he actually knew of Mum Maggie and knew who I was.

'She's not the absolute best and probably won't make a champion. But you would have a great amount of fun showing her.' He explained that my front paws are just a bit too long

I just want to be an athlete!

I am NOT a showgirl!!

and that I probably hold them too close together. Personally, I think that's from all the footballing I do. And he thought I might not be quite big enough in the chest, which again for a footballer, or a golfer, isn't a bad thing. He suggested that my owner should phone Mrs Cole and ask if we could come along to watch one of the Cardigan corgi shows. I was just so excited to meet him, and my owner seemed quite thrilled. He said that he used to judge Cardigan corgis and Mrs Cole would know who he was. He added that I had the most beautiful face and now he could see the real resemblance with Mum Maggie.

We were both so delighted and I felt really proud. We returned to the ring for the last three classes. The first one was for the dog with the nicest eyes. This seemed a bit of a lottery. There were at least thirty dogs in the class and again I got to the final line-up. Once more, there were no prizes or rosettes for me. But my thoughts had turned to Mum Maggie and meeting her again.

And then it *was* my turn. This class was for Dog and Owner Most Bonded. Owners sat with their dogs and their dogs responded and some did little party tricks. But my owner had other ideas. She sat cross-legged, held a little white Polo mint in her mouth and, as the judge watched, I just eased it gently, gently into my mouth giving my owner a kiss as I did it. The judge was bowled over and now I was the winner – or at least, we were both the winners.

Waiting for my classes!

The last class with a different judge was really horrible. This was for the dog that the judge would most like to take home. I hadn't realised that there was a possibility I might have to go home with the judge and wouldn't be going home with my owner. I thought we were here for fun and not with any possibility of my being given away or sold. I certainly didn't want to be the dog that this judge would want to take home with him. As he came up and looked at me I tried to make myself look as unattractive as possible. I stood with my front paws as close together as I could, let my tail flop, stuck back my ears, raised the left corner of my lip and tried to look as unpleasant as a little Cardigan corgi could possibly look.

I was absolutely horrified when the judge pulled me forward as the winner. They announced very loudly over the Tannoy, 'The judge has chosen the dog he would most like to take home.'

I snarled, pulled a face, did a little wee, and the judge obviously changed his mind about taking me home. He presented my owner with a large red rosette and then walked away. That told him!

'Well done, Annika. You might be the dog the judge most wants to take home but rest assured you're coming back home with me. We'll celebrate with sardines and an egg.'

And then I forgot all the words of wisdom from Miss Ingrid's School of Correction. I spotted a small boy with a football, ran after it, stole the football and nudged it into the goal. The little boy was crying, which I thought was rather unsporting. But I

Suddenly I just couldn't resist the football!

heard my owner shout, 'Annika, come,' extremely loudly, so I shot back to her side and stood to attention. She buckled me into my blue safety harness, sat me on the front seat of the car and we waved goodbye to my first dog show.

17

It's Mum Maggie

'Hello, is that Mrs Cole? Remember me? I bought Annika from you. No, there's nothing wrong with Annika. She's an absolute joy.' Then she explained how we had met Mr P at the dog show and he had suggested that my owner might enjoy showing me. I could hear just one side of the conversation, of course, but I could guess what was being said.

'No, I know you didn't sell her to me as a show dog. Yes, of course she's just a pet, and she's becoming a really good golfing dog, but it might be nice for her to see some other Cardigan corgis and it would be fun for both of us.'

With that I gathered we were going to visit a dog show for Cardigan corgis only. I didn't know whether there would be classes for those with best ears, or the waggiest tail. I didn't really know what it would be about at all. Perhaps there would be a class for those that were best with a football.

The morning of the show arrived. I was going along as a spectator but my owner brushed me and combed me and made me look just as grand as possible. I travelled in my blue harness in the front of the car and my owner, having forgotten Miss Ingrid's words of wisdom, carried on her usual conversation with Sidney Satnav until we found the hall.

When we arrived, I couldn't believe it – so many dogs just

like me. Some were black and white with brindle bits, like me; others were dark brown or speckled brown, and there were even a few lovely blue merles, like the picture of my dad. I just couldn't believe it. There were Cardigan corgis everywhere.

My owner and I were both a bit shy but we needn't have worried. We were soon descended upon, even if only to buy raffle tickets. Mrs Cole was over in the corner of the hall and was obviously in charge of something.

And then, joy of joys, I spotted her, over the other side of the hall – Mum Maggie. Obviously, I knew it was her straight away. My owner didn't realise. And a kind lady with three Cardigan corgis asked who we were. I explained to her girls and boys with a few quick woofs that I was one of Maggie's daughters and wanted to go to see her. Mrs Cole was still busy.

I managed to pull my owner round the other side of the hall. Mum Maggie was sitting in a big cage, and I gave a can-I-sit-with-her woof, and a little it's-my-Mum woof, so that my owner cottoned on and popped me in with Mum Maggie. Well, we had so much to woof about.

'Oh Annika, my poppet, you look wonderful. What a gorgeous face. You were always my favourite. And fancy you coming to a show. We only ever thought of you as a pet dog, but my goodness, aren't you a treasure.'

I explained to Mum Maggie virtually everything I had been doing from the day we left. I told her about Edward and Sophie and playing golf and my friend Barney and how I was becoming a real expert with a small ball and a football. I told

There's my mum Maggie!

her about our visit to Cumbria and how I heard the man in the pub talking about brother Bryn and how well he was doing with sheep and cattle.

'Oh Mum, it's so good to see you. We met a lovely man at a village dog show who said he thought I might have won best puppy. He talked to my owner and said that I wouldn't ever be a real champion but she could probably enjoy showing me.'

Mum Maggie was so pleased to see me. She had some news of Emily and told me that Kiki was obviously going to be a real champion in Finland. She had heard through the grapevine that brother Totti was having a great time in Finland. She knew a bit about Toby, but now with my news of brother Bryn, she knew where all her puppies were. She was delighted.

It was just like old times. She gave my ears a good wash,

checked out my paws and my toes and really just gave me a good going over, like in my puppy days. We cuddled up together in the cage, woofing on and on and exchanging news. And then standing in front of us was Mrs Cole.

'Is that you, Annika? Oh my goodness, Maggie, hasn't she got a pretty face. You were always my favourite in that litter, never going to be a champion but just the gamest, funniest, cleverest puppy Maggie produced.'

I felt so proud and so happy. It was going to be sad when I had to leave Mum Maggie and go home but I hoped that we would meet again.

People came to talk to us and corgis came and woofed at us. Several people already seemed to know about me and would ask if I was Annika.

It was nearly time for Mum Maggie to show in her class. She won. I watched intently to see what she did. She looked so long and low and just glided round as though she was on little wheels. Would I ever be able to do that?

My owner had a cup of tea and a sausage roll; I had a drink of water and a bit of the sausage roll. Mrs Cole started talking to my owner about the possibility of my being shown.

'Now you do realise, don't you, that Annika isn't a real show dog. Yes, she's extremely good and has the prettiest face, but she won't make a champion like Maggie. So you mustn't be disappointed.'

I was just so happy to see Mum Maggie again and hoped perhaps I would see Emily one day. It wasn't really about winning or losing. Playing golf was all about winning or

Mum says I'm the prettiest of her puppies

It's me!

losing; not this. My owner collected some little booklets about shows and arranged to take me to one.

To make the day really special we won two prizes in the raffle, a bottle of wine and a pack of soaps. Two of the owners were discussing how they had both won raffle prizes. One was a squeaky ball and the other a furry pheasant.

'My girl certainly won't play with a squeaky ball,' said one. 'My boy certainly doesn't want a furry pheasant,' said the other. I really could have hugged my owner so hard when she said to them, 'Oh, would you like to swap them for a bottle of wine and some nice French soap? My Annika will just love the squeaky ball and the furry pheasant.'

I woofed a fond farewell to Mum Maggie and another to Mrs Cole. My owner seemed delighted. I rode home on the front seat in my blue harness. All the others left the show in their crates in the back of their cars, so that made me feel good. My owner talked to me and talked to Sidney Satnav, just as Miss Ingrid had told her not to do. But I knew I would be in strict training when we got home.

We went to visit Barney and his owner on the way back.

'How was the show?'

'Annika did so well. We won a lovely squeaky ball and a furry pheasant.'

I winked at Barney and he winked back.

'Was it in a raffle?' he woofed.

'It might have been! You can share my furry pheasant and I'll tell you one day.'

With my prize pheasant

18

The Danger of Cheese

My owner and I worked at least three times a day, using Miss Ingrid's instructions – up and down, up and down, sit and stay and come to the whistle, sit to the whistle, stay like a statue, and come to the whistle like a bat out of hell. Often the last session would be late at night, before bedtime.

And then one night the floodlights came on and there was the big, black dragon, back again, patrolling and taunting me from the other side of the water. I rushed to see it, forgetting all my good manners and training, and barked to alert my owner to its presence. She came to stand beside me and there were two dragons. One had huge ears and the other was tall with waving arms. Edward cosied up beside her, and suddenly a third, rather small dragon appeared, to make up a menacing trio.

I barked and looked up at my owner for comfort. I started to run and the big-eared dragon ran.

'Oh Annika, you silly bunny. It's your own shadow. Watch me.' And we all ran to the left. Or at least, we both ran to the left and Edward sauntered behind us. 'Watch, Annika.'

I was still to be convinced. But I remembered what Edward had said about me being frightened of my own shadow. I had always thought of Shadow as the farmer's lovely dog, who lived over the road from Mrs Cole. Oh, how stupid I've been! Edward was trying to hiss at me, 'I told you so, you silly dog.' We stood there in a line again, my owner waving her arms to demonstrate the shadow while I tilted my head, just to check matters over once more.

I have to say that I was very proud of the new, disciplined me. I hugged closely to my owner's left leg to the point of almost tripping her up. At the Cambridge Puppy and Junior Classes, we excelled. My owner refused to use titbits, believing, as Miss Ingrid had impressed, on pride of performance. But as the field was paved with cheese this wasn't a problem. I flew through my bronze and silver obedience awards, my nose virtually attached to my owner's left leg, particularly if she wore shorts and had rubbed on a little cream cheese at nose height.

I didn't have much chance of becoming a herding dog, despite collecting all my toys and putting them in a tidy heap in the middle of the garden.

I really wanted to be a gundog and retrieve. My owner taught me to sit and stay while she threw away my dumbbell, and to rush to retrieve it only when told. I understood quite clearly the difference between a squeaky or rubber ball, which could be retrieved when thrown, a dumbbell, which couldn't be retrieved until commanded, and a golf ball, which mustn't be touched at all (except in a moment of real weakness when out of sight).

I think I was a little bit of a figure of fun at the dog-training class. Somehow, I could never keep up with the dog in front. That was because of the cheese, the gorgeous cheese. What was the point of having your nose up the tail or bottom of the dog in front when you could have your nose on the ground, sniffing out lumps of abandoned cheese? My owner kept having to urge me to move along. Pat, the trainer, would patiently wait for me as the class slowcoach. I usually found myself as tailend Charlie in most of the walk-to-heel formations. I was usually the last to sit down in musical chairs; I was usually the last to lie flat on the 'down' command. I don't quite know why. On the golf course or in the garden I would respond in a flash. In hindsight, it must have been the cheese scattered in that lovely, smelly field.

One Saturday morning, I was being particularly sluggish. The cheese had got the better of me, and I had been celebrating on a drop of Bovril the night before. By this time, we were practising lying flat on the ground while our owners stood fifteen paces away. We each had to lie flat, without dozing off, and then rush back to our owners, one by one, as we were called. As usual, I was last in line. I watched the boring old German shepherd rush perfectly to his owner. The miniature dachshund pottered off to his owner, giving the impression of full speed. Even Fred the basset hound lolloped to his master at a fair old jog. And the rest – they all did it. It was hard to concentrate all that time. Other classes were taking place. In one, dogs were doing agility; in another, young puppies were learning baby skills; and in yet another, gundogs were sniffing out fake pheasants and collecting dumbbells.

'Oh Lord, this is boring.' I looked at my owner and gave an enormous I-am-so-bored yawn.

Suddenly, it was my turn to rush to her feet. On her command I dragged myself to my feet. And then I don't know what came over me.

I saw an enormous, black, flat-coated retriever in the gundog class with a huge, red dumbbell. I had to have it. I turned in diagonally the opposite direction from my owner and the trainer, and shot off like greased lightening. My ears were down, my tail was out, my legs, which are too long for me to be a champion corgi, were somehow striding out with the speed I usually saved for the golf course. Off I shot. One man later called me Annika the Exocet Missile. My owner was shouting, 'Annika,' and giving two frantic whistles. I could hear Pat, the trainer, telling my owner to be firm. But I was off. I knew where I was going even if no one else did. I swooped down beside the astonished flat-coated retriever, grabbed his very large, red dumbbell and shot back to my owner. I weaved through the golden retrievers, shot passed Kerman

I can go very, very fast when needed!

173

the German shepherd, vaulted over Franz the dachshund and arrived back at my owner's feet with the prized red dumbbell.

I looked round and the gundogs were amazed. The dog doing agility was standing quite stationary in the middle of the seesaw. The puppies were yelping with excitement. Pat, the trainer, couldn't believe my extraordinary speed. And the gundog trainer began to applaud. Fred, the basset hound, had clearly fallen in love with me but it was unrequited love. I only had eyes for the dumbbell and a nose for the cheese.

I had failed on my final obedience test but my owner seemed so proud that I had demonstrated just how fast a Cardigan corgi can run.

The very next day we started on my show career. Neither my owner nor I had a clue what we were doing. But, fortunately, Mum Maggie was there to give feedback on our performance. At our first show, we walked round the ring just as we had done at obedience class, with my nose virtually glued to my owner's left leg. A little cream cheese had done the trick. I did stand perfectly on the table and I did allow the judge to open my mouth very gently. I showed off my beautiful teeth and looked at the judge intelligently and lovingly, even though I thought she smelt of alcohol. When we did our final line-up for the judge, it was difficult to know what to do. Some owners were kneeling down with their dogs, presumably praying for a good result, while others were standing, holding their dog's head up quite firmly by the lead. My owner simply stood there and I simply stood the best I could, copying Mum Maggie, who was

Mum Maggie gave me lots of coaching

giving me some silent eye and paw signals from outside the ring. We came second and I got a blue rosette.

Mrs Cole tried to give my owner a few tips but my owner explained that she didn't understand the jargon, and the anatomy of a Cardigan corgi was a complete mystery to her. My owner isn't really dim. She was just dim at dog showing. Mum Maggie had far more success with me.

'Look, Annika, your owner is doing all the things that novice owners always do. See that black rubber mat. That's for you to walk on, not for her. But they all do that the first time. Now watch me in my class and see how it's done. You don't walk up close to your owner's leg like an obedience dog. If she wears shorts and puts cream cheese on her leg, for heaven's sake lick it off first before you get in the ring. Now watch what I do. You'll see how I stand well away from my handler so that the judge can see me and not her. And if she does wear trousers instead of shorts, let's hope she has beige or white trousers and not black ones. Pale ones show you up better. Right here I go.'

Mum stood so still on the table and, again, she glided round the ring as though on wheels. There was no wiggling of her body, her back was long and straight, she walked on the mat, lead well away from Mrs Cole. I knew what I had to do. Maggie won a red rosette and a bag of food and I glowed with pride.

'The other thing, Annika, is that you are a slightly long-legged poppet for a show girl. Yes, I know it makes you a brilliant footballer, but judges like to see girls with shorter legs, paws slightly wider apart and a bit bigger in the chest. Your eyes and ears are wonderful and you have the prettiest face of any of my puppies. Now, you've another class at the end of all this for novice handlers. Try to do the best you can for your owner. Remember, get those feet wider apart when the judge inspects you. Puff out your chest and let the judge adore you.'

I strutted round the ring with my owner, walking farther away from her than before and staying firmly on the rubber mat while she walked on the floor. When we stood to look our very best, I remembered to put my front paws out wider, puff out my chest and keep my eyes firmly on the judge so that she would be mesmerised into giving me first prize. It was just a class for novice handlers, and the others were either complete duffers, like my owner, or very small children. This time we won and I got a lovely red rosette. My owner won a bag of food and I heard her say it was good and now we could afford to eat again. I hadn't realised that things were that bad but I now knew that I had to work hard, do well at shows and make sure we didn't starve.

I thanked Mum Maggie for all her words of encouragement, and my owner thanked Mrs Cole. We had also won a prize in the raffle, a green-and-white towel with a large red dragon. I later realised that this was quite a status symbol. It was the flag of Wales and we are Welsh corgis. I thought I would probably tell Barney and Edward that I won it as a prize and hoped my owner would lie to Barney's owner so that we shared the same untruth.

I thought I would enjoy dog shows. It wasn't just because of the rosettes and the prizes but because of exchanging news about Bryn and Toby and Kiki and the rest of the gang with Mum Maggie. I think she missed me and I really missed her, even though I have a lovely home and a smashing love/hate relationship with Edward.

On the way home, my owner stopped at the supermarket and did a really big shop. I watched her come out with a trolley laden full of cleaning things and food things and fruit and clanking bottles. She had bought so much stuff that it filled three jumbo-sized yellow bags; not just those floppy white plastic carrier bags but the big sturdy, stout ones that you use time and again.

The owner parked her car on our drive and lifted me safely out on to the gravel. I had my blue rosette attached to my collar; the red one was pinned on my little holdall. Edward said my blue rosette made me look like a Conservative Party candidate (whatever that meant). He jumped in the car to inspect my cage and I told him, quite untruthfully, that I had won the green, white and red dragon towel for obedience.

My owner brought the shopping into the kitchen, locked the car and picked up the phone. I heard her telling Barney's owner that we had got a red rosette and a blue rosette and a bag of food and that we had won a red, white and green Welsh flag towel. I hoped she would reinforce the lie I had told Edward and say it was for obedience, which she did. Yippee!

Then temptation got the better of me again. I had heard on the radio about temptation and Adam and Eve in the Garden of Eden and how Adam couldn't resist biting into the apple. Well, for me, it was cheese. As if transported by a miracle, and I don't really know how, I found myself in the middle of the lawn with a large lump of cheese, which I later discovered to be Danish blue. It was just completely and utterly, mind-blowingly, ear-dazzlingly, tail-wagglingly gorgeous. It was worth all the effort of nibbling away at the clingfilm wrapper. Was it a large piece? Was it a small piece? I suppose it was about twice the size of my owner's fist.

I was able to compare those two sizes quite easily when she rushed out of the house, shouting my name and waving her fist. When she stuck two fingers in her mouth and made an ear-splitting whistle, I knew I should stop. But as Edward

Ed says I look like a Tory candidate

said later, it would be easier to catch a rainbow than to catch a Cardigan corgi with a piece of cheese. It is quite possible to run right round our house. It didn't matter how much my owner called me or chased me, I was obsessed with the cheese and hanging on to it and eating it, clingfilm and all.

Suddenly, it had all gone. I stood and looked at my owner and wished I hadn't done it.

'Oh, Annika. What have you done? You naughty girl.'

Things moved very quickly. She lured me into the kitchen with a biscuit, captured me on my lead and shut me in my cage. Then she made a quick phone call and I was whisked off into the car. Before I realised what was happening, we were outside the vet's office. The vet wasn't there but she soon arrived. She

Well done Annika

didn't speak like everyone else I knew. I think she must have been foreign.

'Anneeeeka. What have you done wiz zee cheese? Yes, Anneeeeka must stay in overnight until zee cheese has gone. It may come out zee mouth; it may come out zee bottom. But wiz zee clingfilm, it must go. Please ring in zee morning to find out when to collect her.'

I stayed in overnight. Apparently, it was a very special piece of Danish blue cheese. My owner told Barney's owner that at £75 it was the most expensive piece of cheese she had ever bought. I know I had to take nasty medicine and I know I puked up lots of the cheese and also had a sore bottom in the morning. I don't remember much more about it.

But the vet did remember me. The next time I saw her, about a year later, she said, 'Ah yes, Anneeeeka. I remember zee terrible smell and the Danish blue cheese priced at 98 pence.'

'Actually,' said my owner, '£75.98p.' A very expensive piece of cheese!

19

Christmas Cheer

It was just after Christmas and it had snowed very heavily. I loved Christmas.

My owner gave Edward a lovely red-and-white bib with the words 'I Love Christmas' written on it. She persuaded him to pose for a Christmas picture wearing the bib, sitting by a bottle of champagne and with his head and right paw firmly in the bowl of sprouts. It became the next year's Christmas card and recipients were amazed at how a cat could like sprouts. A cat would unquestionably like sprouts if the sprouts were sitting on smelly, oily sardines. It was easy.

Sophie, who is easy to forget because she spends her life hiding behind her tail, received presents of new toys that dangled on elastic from the banisters.

And as for me, I received a whole parcel of squeaky balls. I never bite them or damage them, but I do lose them, usually in water. The postman arrived with a large package for me, which, by Edward's reckoning, contained twenty-four squeaky balls in various colours and with different faces. We knew it was squeaky balls when the postman brought it up the drive because he carried the parcel under his arm and it squeaked all the way.

Happy Christmas, Edward

Christmas – I feel ridiculous!

I also had presents of a new collar, a new rope gundog lead, several chewy bones and a ball on the end of a rope. My owner bought me a set of reindeer antlers with flashing lights and jingling bells. Under the Christmas tree, I spotted a parcel labelled 'Annika from Edward'. It smelt like chocolates and I resisted opening it all the way until Christmas morning. Then, before my owner was up and about, I ripped off the paper and the label and sure enough it was chocolates. I was suspicious that my owner had bought the present. Firstly, Edward doesn't have pocket money. Secondly, although he often sits on the keys of the laptop computer, I don't think he could order anything over the internet. And thirdly, Edward can't keep a secret and if he had bought it, he would have told me. Fourthly, and being a real detective, like you see on the television, I also noticed that there was a present signed to Edward from me

Sprouts for all at Christmas

and another to Sophie from me. I hadn't been shopping. I guessed that our owner was trying to make us appreciate each other as friends.

The present that I had supposedly bought for Sophie smelt very like special cat biscuits. It sat on the bottom branches of the Christmas tree, right at nose level. I guessed that Sophie probably didn't know it was there, and what she didn't know about she wouldn't miss. Somehow, in nudging the little parcel with my nose, it fell to the floor. And in trying to tidy it, the wrapping paper fell off. I was just about to chew through the plastic packaging and find the biscuits when I remembered the episode of the cheese and the trip to the vet's. I couldn't manage to wrap up the biscuits again, so I tried to bury them under a rug but that didn't work.

I thought it was essential that I didn't get the blame for this misdemeanour and that Edward did. I saw him come strutting round the corner, looking terribly important and flicking his tail. I put one paw firmly on the corner of the little packet and bit off the other corner, carefully spitting it out. I tipped them out on to the floor in front of Edward, resisted eating any of them and made sure Edward looked the culprit. Sure enough, our owner came in to find Edward happily munching away on Sophie's present and me sitting like an angel on the chair.

'Oh you two, you really are a pair of scoundrels. Now Sophie hasn't got a present from you, Annika.'

I couldn't really understand how our owner could think I was implicated in this theft. And then Edward, being very perceptive, pointed out that I had a piece of red string with a label saying 'To Sophie from Annika', hanging round my right ear.

I already knew what my main present was – the big packet of squeaky balls. I ripped open the packaging, as I was supposed to do, and out they all fell, rolling all over the floor. Edward and Sophie both rushed at them and patted them about. But cats have very small spans of concentration – apart from when they stare at people – and were bored with the squeaky balls within a few seconds. I rolled on them, trod on them and they squeaked and talked and sang to me.

'It might be a nice gesture to give one to Barney. After all, he *is* your best friend.'

A very happy Christmas!

But then I had another parcel. This was a large, square box and I just knew it would be a big box of dried fish sticks. I started ripping at the corners of the box but it didn't smell like fish sticks. I ripped off some more and it didn't smell like biscuits. In fact, it smelt like rubber. I had an awful feeling the owner had bought me a set of four pink Wellington boots for going out in the snow, which lay thick on the ground, so I more or less lost interest in the parcel but thought I must be polite. Eventually, the box was open and there it was – not four pink Wellington boots, but a beautiful black-and-white basketball. The basketball, you will remember, is more robust than a plastic football and less likely to be punctured by naughty teeth. I managed to rip off all the paper and release the ball so that it danced and bounced into the middle of the squeaky balls.

'There, Annika, what do you think of that?'

Well, really, what a stupid question. I was in seventh heaven. My owner opened the door and flung out the football. (I preferred to call it a football, even though it wasn't.) I chased out after the ball and pushed it on the firm white snow. Edward and Sophie both walked out and at the feel of the snow shook their paws disapprovingly. They tiptoed about, raising their paws with ridiculous high steps, looking thoroughly affected and quite absurd.

I pushed the football round with my nose and my paws and it gathered snow. I pushed it this way and that way, nudging it to the left and nudging it to the right. Ball control of my precious football was absolutely crucial so that it didn't escape down into the water. My owner came out to play with me and kicked the football and threw the squeaky balls and also made balls of snow, which disintegrated on the ground as they landed.

Barney came to visit and so did my friend Henry, the springer spaniel. I rolled in the snow and got thoroughly wet and then lay with my paws in the air. Barney said he thought I must have been drinking too much, had a hangover and eaten too much Christmas cake. Henry ran round sniffing everything in sight and then suddenly disappeared. Oh my goodness, he had gone down to the water and hadn't come back. He must have drowned. I ran over to the top of the bank to look down into the water to find him. I didn't know if Henry could swim.

I had been very drunk at Christmas with too much cheese and cake!

I just love the snow!

But all the water had gone, replaced by solid ground, and there was Henry racing around on the snow where the water should have been. Barney soon joined Henry and they raced up and down, up and down, madly chasing each other and sniffing things, like boys do. Henry cocked his leg to prove he had been there and Barney followed suit. Then Barney cocked his leg and Henry followed him. What silly creatures! I returned to my footballing practice only to nudge the ball too firmly and see it shoot away on to the snow where the water should have been. Henry and Barney were still chasing up and down the little snowed-over river.

'Come and play on the ice, Annika. We can play football here.'

The football moved much more quickly on the ice than it did on the snow. In fact, it moved much more quickly on the ice than it did on grass. Up and down we went, pushing it this way and that. I found four more squeaky balls that I had lost during the summer. They had escaped down to the edge of the water and now I could reach them from the ice. I spoke to each in turn, ran across the ice with them and dropped them back on to the snow-covered lawn.

Yes, this was the game for me – not just football but football on ice.

The snow and ice stayed for a couple of weeks. Barney and Henry came to visit again and we played on the ice and up and down the banks, sometimes with the squeaky ball but usually with the football. I just loved it. I was much better at football than either of those two were.

'Too tall. You're too tall, boys. Get your nose down and push the ball around like this. Right paw, left paw and nudge with your nose. Come on, Henry, concentrate.'

Barney tried to look very glamorous as a footballer and Henry kept getting side-tracked to sniff his surroundings. This was my game. Football. Wonderful football. And then it happened. There was a sharp little pain in my back leg. Ow! I gave a my-goodness-that-hurt woof and rushed back up on to the snow-covered lawn. I gave a please-come-and-help-me woof and thought I needed to show my owner what I had done. But it was all too obvious. I must have broken my leg playing football on the ice.

It was off to the vet's again, not to the French lady vet who had removed my stolen Danish blue cheese and clingfilm, but to our lovely, cuddly man vet.

'I think she has an injury to the cruciate ligament. I think we need to refer her to the specialist in Newmarket.'

Off we went to the veterinary hospital where they looked at my poor, broken right leg. The receptionist and nurses were terribly kind. And each remarked that they had never seen a Cardigan corgi before. I had to stay in overnight for an operation and I saw my owner cry when she left me.

I don't remember anything about the operation. I think they made me feel drowsy and go to sleep and have sweet dreams while they repaired my damaged leg. The whole of my leg was put in plaster and I was a given a funny collar to wear like a lampshade so that I couldn't possibly bite off the dressings.

Eventually, my owner arrived to collect me and to discuss my injury with the vet. 'Firstly, the good news, Annika hasn't broken her leg. Secondly, we've been able to repair it completely and she should be absolutely as good as new. She has completely damaged the cruciate ligament in that right leg. It's a very unusual injury for a dog of this size and I've never heard of one in a Cardigan corgi.

'You must have heard about this type of injury several times this winter,' the vet went on. My owner shook her head. 'It's the footballers' injury; it's the one the footballers get. Two England players had this same injury just last week.'

A real footballing dog with a real footballing injury. I must ask Edward whether the England players have to wear upside down lampshades on their heads.

20

I Fall in Love

Christmas had come and gone and the snow was melting. My football sat up on a shelf in the kitchen well out of reach. With my leg still in plaster I was restricted to walks on the lead and gentle exercise. I didn't like being an invalid. Golfing members and visitors kindly asked after my health. Some would ask why my head was in a bucket while others called it a lampshade. What did make me proud was when my owner said I'd had a footballing accident, 'just like an England footballer'. That made me feel a little better. They would look on me as an athlete.

My bottom is getting very cold!

Although, with my gammy leg, I couldn't be shown, my owner took me to a Cardigan corgi show for a day out. As a treat we went in her blue sports car. I sat on a sheepskin rug on the front seat in a new red safety harness I'd acquired at Christmas. The car went vroom, vroom and I rather liked the speed. My owner had told me very firmly not to nibble at my leg. So I was a bit cross when we arrived at the show and she made me wear the bucket.

'There, Annika. Now they'll realise you're invalided and not for showing.'

Since my leg was bound in blue plaster and I was hobbling a bit, I did think the bucket was overkill. Actually, it was a nuisance. I do quite pride myself on being able to catch a biscuit better than most. The bucket got in the way of my vision. On one occasion when, very unusually, I missed the biscuit, it stayed in the bucket, rattling around under my chin.

Anyway, we walked into the hall and people were kind and greeted us. My owner, after lots of socialising with other owners, sat down near the side of the ring, ready to watch the action. I could see Mrs Cole but she hadn't yet seen us. Perhaps she was too ashamed to see me in my bucket.

And then I saw Mum Maggie. She gave me a knowing glance from across the hall and a quizzical look to ask what I'd done. I suppose she hadn't heard. If only my owner would take me over to see her. But she was too busy buying raffle tickets. Two six eight white – that was Tom Watson's score when he won the Open Championship at Turnberry in 1977. Five eight seven blue – that was the number of yards by which Lewis

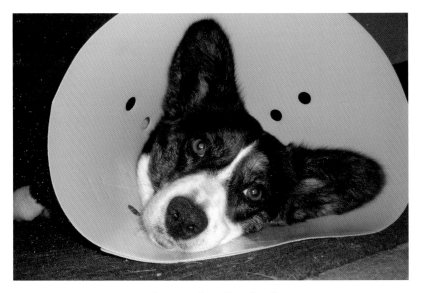

Please get this off my head!

Hamilton won the British Grand Prix. Eighty-three yellow – that was the winning margin when New Zealand beat England at The Oval. Yes, ever since Christmas my owner and I had been mugging up on sporting records. They certainly sounded like lucky numbers to me.

'Well, let's get this show on the road. Who's going to win today?'

And then, joy of joys, I saw him. There, across the hall, just a few yards from Mum Maggie was the boy whom I was sure must be the most handsome Cardigan corgi in the whole world. He was a gorgeous blue merle, just like my dad, Mandylay's Ultimately Blue, whose picture hung in our kitchen. My goodness, wasn't this fellow stunning. I looked at his wonderful ears and his shiny attentive eyes. I was in love.

And then I thought how he really mustn't see me like this,

in this dreadful bucket. How could he cosy up and meet me when I looked so ridiculous? I looked up at my owner as if to say, 'Please take off the bucket,' but she had eyes only for the raffle tickets and sausage rolls at the food counter. It isn't done to make noises or woofs at shows so I had to be very careful. I tried to make a little woof that sounded like clearing my throat, just to attract her attention. Please release me from the bucket. But she didn't.

Given the circumstances, I decided it was best to hide behind my owner's legs so that this handsome boy wouldn't see me looking so ridiculous. I glanced across at Mum Maggie, and waggled my head a little, hoping she would come and rescue me and take off the bucket. She tugged at Mrs Cole, looked up at her, looked over to me, looked up at Mrs Cole again and shook her head. By this time my owner was thrilled at her success in the raffle. She had won a bottle of Baileys, a Cardigan corgi tea towel and a packet of cheese biscuits, which I thought I might enjoy.

'Oh how lovely to see you. Now how is Annika doing?'

Fortunately, Mum Maggie conveyed to them both that they needed to take off my bucket. Gosh, that felt better. I couldn't wait to ask Mum Maggie all about that handsome blue merle boy on the other side of the hall. Like all girls with their mums, I felt a bit embarrassed telling her I was in love with him.

'Oh, he's Ace. He's really the most handsome blue merle that anyone could ever see. He should be a real champion but he has a terrible problem.'

I was crestfallen to think Ace might have some real defect.

'He just won't stay quiet while he's being shown. Everyone thinks he's growling and people are terrified of him but really he's just so happy and wags his tail and sings and purrs like a cat. But it's a real no-no for a show boy.'

By this time our owners were dragging Mum Maggie and me round the other side of the hall to meet Ace. I wanted to look just as beautiful as I could for the first moment I met him. I opened my eyes wide; I pricked up my ears to their full magnificence and swished out my tail. I didn't want Ace to think I was flat-chested. I didn't think I could emulate Dolly Parton, whom I'd seen on the television over Christmas, but I did the best I could.

Mum Maggie kindly introduced me to Ace. 'This is Annika, the pretty girl I've been telling you about, who had the accident playing football.'

'Hello, I'm Ace. I'm in such trouble and it's awful that you should meet me at this show. I'm really quite fussed about my

It's Ace – love at first sight!

toenails and my teeth and my tail and I do so want to make a good impression. The problem is that I give in to temptation and I just can't stop making silly noises when they put me on the table. I hope you won't feel ashamed of me if I don't do well. This is my absolute last chance at being a show boy. I just can't help it and I don't know what comes over me. I think I'm just a typical Welshman, born to sing. Oh goodness, now it's my class and here comes my handler.'

'I do hope Ace is all right,' Mum Maggie confided to me. 'He's so nervous. Let's watch how he does. If only he could stop that silly purring he would be one of the greatest blue merle champions there has ever been.'

There were lots of people in the hall, looking after their dogs and buying raffle tickets, and collecting their prizes and getting their own dogs ready for showing. I just crossed my paws to wish Ace luck. He walked round the ring looking magnificent. What a boy! And then his handler put him on the table.

What was that dreadful noise? The whole hall started rumbling. A man said he thought it was an earthquake and went to dive under a table. Someone else said it was the old oil-fired boiler and rickety central heating and why hadn't the Church Commissioners done something to rectify it. The lady behind me asked me what the noise was and said it sounded like an underground train at Paddington Station. Nobody, except Maggie and me, realised it was Ace. His tail was wagging, his ears were pointed and he was just purring. The judge was very apprehensive about looking in his mouth but his handler assured the judge that Ace was purring through happiness and the noise was not aggressive growling. Ace smiled the most gorgeous smile, showed his teeth and the judge quickly took his handler's word for it that the noise was a happy one.

The handler said afterwards that it was touch and go whether Ace was removed from the ring and disqualified from being shown for life. Ace was so deflated that he cocked his leg by the table where the man who thought it was an earthquake was hiding.

'There, Maggie and Annika, that's me finished for showing. After all that practice on the patio table at home, I failed everybody. Temptation just got to me and look what a fool I made of myself.'

I just wanted to cuddle up to Ace and tell him he was the most handsome boy at the show and I didn't care whether he was to be a champion or not. Maggie told him that he was a silly sausage and it didn't matter if he wasn't a champion. She explained that I wouldn't be a champion either, not because I made silly noises, but because my legs are a little long and my chest a little flat.

'But the good news, Annika, is that Ace is going to come to live with me. Although his present owners love him dearly, they do so want a boy who can be a champion. So when you come to visit, which hopefully you will, you'll see lots more of Ace.'

My owner and Mrs Cole were discussing how I could always go and stay with Mrs Cole whenever my owner went on holiday. 'We'd absolutely love to have Annika staying with us any time. She's no trouble at all, and Maggie and she get on like a house on fire. And then, of course, I'll be having Ace

Dreaming of Ace and lots of puppies!

living with us as well. No, any time you go on holiday, just bring Annika over to us and we'll look after her. And really Annika and Ace would make a lovely couple, you know. Who knows, perhaps there could be pups in the future.'

I was in seventh heaven. I had met the boy of my dreams. He could sing like an angel and make a grown man hide under a table. He was definitely the boy for me. I sat proudly in the front of the car on my sheepskin rug, wearing my lovely red harness, looking out to woof goodbye to Maggie and Ace. She was concentrating on me with a little see-you-soon woof. Ace, being a typical boy, was simply woofing 'nice car!'

When we arrived home, Edward was there to greet us and did a naughty little spray on the front number plate. He knew the car well enough but I think it was just jealousy that he hadn't been allowed out in it. I started to tell him about Ace but he wasn't really interested. It was probably because I said Ace purred louder than any cat; I suppose that was a little bit humiliating for Edward.

The Baileys, the Cardigan corgi tea towel and the packet of cheese biscuits were brought in and Edward said, 'You can't tell me you won those today, Annika. You weren't even competing.'

And then I heard my owner on the phone to Barney's owner. 'A bottle of Baileys, a Cardigan corgi tea towel and a packet of cheese biscuits, which I thought you and Barney might like to share. No, of course we didn't win them in the show. Annika wasn't competing. This is the one show of the year where they have a raffle to raise money.'

I knew that was a lie because they always had a raffle but we always pretended that the raffle prize was won for excellence

I was in love with Ace – but all he said was 'Nice car'

and not just luck. My owner told Mrs Cole that that was what golfers do all the time.

I could hear my owner telling Barney's owner that they were trying to do some matchmaking between Ace and me.

'Yes, when the time is right, they could apparently have the most gorgeous puppies. You know we've got a kennel name already for when Annika does have puppies.' This was the first I knew of that and the first inkling I had that I might eventually have puppies.

'Of course, she won't be able to have puppies for many months yet, perhaps even a year. Oh yes, her kennel name is Wildcard. That's right, Card, as in Cardigan. Well I thought it was quite a clever name, too. Think of all the lovely golfing names we could have. Wildcard Faldo, Wildcard Nicklaus, Wildcard Watson, Wildcard Woods.'

As far as I was concerned, any puppies of mine would have footballing names. There'd be Wildcard Beckham, Wildcard Rooney, Wildcard Lineker and Wildcard Shearer.

My owner continued prattling on to Barney's owner. 'Girls' names? If she has a girl puppy, she's going to be called Wildcard Maggie after her wonderful mum.' I thought that was a wonderful idea. Wouldn't Mum Maggie be proud of that?

My owner and I cuddled up on the sofa beside the fire to watch the television. I was in love; deeply, passionately, and absolutely in love with Ace. I'd always thought love films on the television were sloppy and a waste of time. But I was soon out for the count, happily dreaming of Ace and cuddling and puppies. Happy days.

21

On Display at Crufts

Soon it was time for Crufts, the greatest dog show on earth. I was going as a special guest to man the Cardigan corgi stand with my owner. I told Edward and Barney that I couldn't compete because I'd had the bad leg. In fact, I couldn't compete because I hadn't been good enough to qualify, but I wasn't going to tell them that.

This was going to be a big day. I didn't really know what to expect. I'd heard our postlady proudly telling my owner that her retriever had qualified for Crufts. And other people would say, in hushed tones, that they knew of someone who had a dog that was going to Crufts. I knew it was very, very important.

Two days before we were due to go to the show, my owner gave me a good brushing and cut my toenails. I really hate having that done. If only I could climb trees like Edward, I'm sure my claws would stay short. I wonder if dogs at Crufts have lovely nail varnish like the owner's housekeeper wears on her toes. That would look smart instead of having to have them filed down.

The clippers are bad enough but then my owner uses an electric buzz-buzz. She held me on her lap and then buzzed away at each of my toenails. It didn't hurt. She's always very gentle. But it tickled and the noise was really irritating. I see the greenkeepers on the golf course wearing big flaps over their ears. It's something to do with keeping noise out. I wish I could have the same when my owner uses the buzz-buzz.

Then I had my tummy all washed and cleaned and my owner brushed me from top to tail; in fact from tail to top. She dried me with the hairdryer, which I don't mind. It's nothing like as bad as the buzz-buzz and nowhere near as frightening as the vaccy or the noise of the microwave.

Show dogs aren't supposed to wear collars in case it ruckles up their fur. So for the week before Crufts I had no collar on at all. I felt a bit insecure without my name badge and telephone number. Suppose I got lost. Who would know where I came from? Anyway, I hadn't got lost and it was just about time for Crufts. I heard my owner talking to Barney's owner about the show.

Getting spruced up ready for Crufts

'Apparently, they have loads of stalls and you can buy just about anything to do with dogs. And there are agility, flyball and obedience competitions, and all sorts of other things to watch. We're going on the day when the corgis are being shown, helping to man the Cardigan corgi stand. Yes, every breed has a show stand. People can visit, find out about the dogs and ask the owners all about them. All the posh dogs and champions will be in the show ring, so we'll be almost on our own on the stand. Well, I hope Annika is good with children. I can't imagine she wouldn't be. It's all very exciting and I'll let you know how we get on.'

Crufts is held in Birmingham and, as a treat, we travelled there in the owner's blue sports car. I hoped we'd meet up with Ace again because he really liked the car, and possibly he'd like me. This time I hadn't got the bucket on my head and my leg was out of plaster and well mended.

Once we had parked the car, we had to wait to get on a bus. I'd never been on a bus before; what an adventure! Loads of owners and dogs were doing the same thing, on their way to the show. Some people had their dogs in cages, balanced on trolleys, which they were pushing along. The dogs looked a bit daft, sitting in their cages. I hoped I never had to do that. Some others had their fur all tied back with ribbons and I saw a couple of enormous dogs with boots on all their feet. I just had my gundog rope lead. Would I be smart enough?

We made our way into the show and I couldn't believe it. There were dogs everywhere – tiny dogs, big dogs, all sorts of breeds that I'd never seen before. There were stands full of

Do the Queen's Pembroke corgis travel in such style?

clothes for people and stands full of coats for dogs, and all sorts of leads and cages and things for being washed with. A couple of stands had special hairdryers; another had treadmills for dogs, rather like the owner's jogging machine. I was beginning to wonder what I was letting myself in for.

And then I saw all these rows of stands, each decorated with pictures of a different dog. There were terriers and hounds and working dogs and gundogs. There were utility dogs and toy dogs and then a section for us, the pastoral or herding dogs. On the way, I saw my friend, Sandy, manning the Skye terrier stand with his owner. Sandy gave me a why-is-he-wearing-a-kilt? woof. This was followed by an I-hope-he-keeps-his-knees-together woof! I could see what Sandy meant; I had never seen a man in a skirt before. I was glad my owner wasn't in fancy dress.

And then, after much searching, we found the Cardigan corgi stand. It was about the size of our study at home and

Sandy the Skye terrier – we meet again!

Meeting my public at Crufts!

had a big pen for dogs and a table for standing on, presumably to kiss the children. The walls of the stand were covered with pictures of Cardigan corgis. Some were herding cattle, others talking to sheep, one was doing obedience in and out of sticks and another was on a seesaw. There were pictures of Cardigan corgis doing absolutely everything – except for playing football. Well, I hoped my owner would put that right for another year. Come on, Newcastle; up the Magpies.

Mrs Cole was there to meet us with Mum Maggie. Mum was far too important to man the stand and, as Mrs Cole explained, Maggie isn't very patient with children. She would probably start yawning.

'Your Annika is going to be an absolute treasure for this. She's got such a wonderful personality and the most beautiful face. The children will just love her.'

I felt quite puffed up with pride. My owner was asking about the other dog who would be joining us.

'I hear a lovely blue merle boy's going to be on the stand with Annika. It isn't by any chance Ace is it? I think Annika's absolutely smitten with him.'

'Good Lord, no. As much as Ace adores children, and adores Annika, that dreadful purring noise of his would probably get us shut down.' Poor Ace had had to be left at home for the day.

'Must go. Keep up the good work. Remember, Annika, eyes and tail, eyes and tail.'

I sat there on the table with my owner close beside it. We were all ready for the doors to open and lots of people to come to see us. I really didn't know what to expect. I started looking around to see what was what. To my left was the stand for the

We met Tammy the Cardigan flyball champion

Swedish vallhunds. They were about my size and seemed quite friendly.

'Oh hello, here's our neighbour, the Cardigan corgi. Who are you? I'm Ingrid.' That brought back memories of Miss Ingrid's School of Correction. I was due to go there for another couple of weeks in the summer.

'Nice to meet you. It's my first time here and I'm a bit nervous. I'm Annika.'

All three Swedish vallhunds started chuckling. 'How can you have a lovely Swedish name like Annika? You should have a Welsh name, like Myfanwy or Tegwen.'

'Yes, Tegwen would be a good Welsh name for a corgi,' chirped another.

'No, I'm Annika, a good Scandinavian name, because both my parents are from Finland. I expect you all know of Annika Sorenstam, the greatest woman golfer there has ever been. Well, I'm a golfing dog.'

'Yes of course we know of Annika Sorenstam. And you're named after her? You can share our water bowl and pigs' ear treats if you like.'

I asked if any of them played golf. They chuckled and said that they didn't. None of them could stay still enough or quiet enough for long enough. They certainly did chunter away during the day.

And then I looked to my right. My goodness, what on earth were these? Small, beige dogs, four of them in all. Two had nice floppy tails and two had no tails at all but just little stubs. They were woofing away and it was difficult to break in, so I looked up at the sign and it said 'Pembroke Corgis'.

As I looked at their stand more closely, I noticed a lovely big picture of the Queen in a yellow dress with a Pembroke corgi sitting beside her. My heart sank. So you mean the Queen didn't have lovely Cardigan corgis like us, but Pembroke corgis?

The world is cruel and life really isn't fair. Why would the Queen have Pembroke corgis and not us? I really did feel very deflated. They had pictures of the Queen's castles decorating their stand, and a poster announcing that two of the corgis who had been in a film with the Queen would be on the stand later. They were such little celebrities and seemed a bit pleased with themselves. They chattered away, woofity-woof, and I couldn't get a word in edgeways.

I sat on my table; my blue-merle partner in crime hadn't arrived by then. Parents with young children came to visit us. My owner assured them I was fine with children and over and over again they wanted their photo taken with me.

'We all know about Pembroke corgis but we had no idea there was another sort of corgi. Aren't they beautiful?' I sat down on the floor with children to have my picture taken; I stood on the table for the older ones. One man asked how heavy I was and my owner plonked me in his arms. I hoped he didn't think she'd given me to him. He was very handsome, though. I heard my owner say very quietly to another lady that he smelt very nice, like Frenchmen always do. I thought it was only dogs who sniffed other dogs. I didn't realise until then that people had the same habits.

Finally, my new friend the blue merle, with the unimaginative name of Blue, arrived to join me. At last I could have a breather and share a bowl of water and a pig's ear chew with the vallhunds.

The Pembroke corgis were still chirruping away. I asked Blue whether he knew why Pembroke corgis didn't have tails and we do. He was older than I was and I thought he would have the answer.

'They say that when the Queen had her first corgi, when she was just a little girl, the corgi did a terrible thing with its tail. It swished it so hard that it knocked a glass of sherry off the coffee table. The Queen was only seven at the time. Her grandmother, Queen Mary, was ever so cross and issued a royal decree that Pembroke corgis would have to have their tails removed at birth.

'You see other dogs with stubby tails. They call them docked. Sometimes spaniels have their tails docked; if they didn't, they would tear them in gorse bushes when they go hunting out the pheasants. For gundogs a docked tail can be safer. But for Pembroke corgis, it was just the fear that they would keep swishing over sherry glasses or coffee cups and upset important elderly ladies.

'And then, almost seventy years after the incident with the sherry glass, another royal decree was issued saying that corgis must have their tails back again. And all the other dogs who had lost their tails celebrated, too. Now, unless they work or hunt, they must keep their tails.'

My owner was very good at talking to all the visitors about Cardigan corgis. She told them I would happily walk four or five miles, but if I didn't get a walk one day, I would just play in the garden or lie on the sofa. I was really proud when she told them how good I was with a football, and an ordinary ball, and even showed them a little film of me on her camera. I loved all the attention. It made me feel really important. The others, including Mum Maggie, might have been off in the show ring, but I was having a whale of a time.

Then my owner just made my day. I heard her say to some people, 'It was absolutely the best day of my life when I chose Annika. She's the most perfect little dog you could ever imagine. I love her to bits; I'd never have another breed of dog after a Cardigan corgi. They really are special.'

My little heart sang with excitement. It turned out to be a really good day, even though Ace wasn't there to share it with me. The kind sponsors of the show gave us all a lovely goody bag, including a big red towel, a big red bowl, a little red pouch for keeping poop bags or treats, a red Frisbee and, best of all, a packet of biscuits. Mum Maggie won her class and sister Emily came third in hers, as a junior, which qualified her to go to Crufts again next year.

Eventually, the show finished. We had miles to walk through various big halls even to get to the bus to get to the car park. Even though Mrs Cole said show dogs shouldn't wear collars, my owner bought me a lovely, red leather one. I did do a little bit of shoplifting at a couple of stands while no one was looking. If they are silly enough to put things at nose height for a Cardigan corgi, they really can't expect us to resist temptation.

The car park was so huge that my owner, like several others, couldn't find her car. She joined forces with another lady. My owner held her dog and me while the lady went off to search for her car, which she eventually found, and then she came back to hold on to me so that my owner could find ours. I tried to give an I-know-where-the-car-is woof but my owner didn't listen. If I tip my head on one side just to show I've understood her, why can't she tip her head to the side to show she's understood me? Anyway, she found our car, hiding among the vans. The sports car is called Nigel. I'm sure if she'd had the good sense to take me with her, I could have found him much earlier. Or if she had simply called to Nigel, he might have made a peep-peep to let us know where he was. He does sometimes make peep-peeps and flash his lights all on his own. But anyway, we were all safely reunited and drove home.

Now that's more like it! Kitted up for the ride home!

Edward greeted us as usual, by spraying the front number plate of the car.

'Oh, Edward, we've had such a grand day. Mum Maggie had all the effort of being shown and simply won a red rosette and a card but just look what I got given. There's a red towel, a red bowl, the red pouch, the poop bags and all the other goodies.' Edward said he thought I probably shoplifted the lot but calmed down when my owner gave him a new bouncy elastic toy and some lamb-flavoured cat biscuits.

We watched the final of Crufts on TV the next day. A very special Cardigan corgi friend of mine, Ina, had beaten all the other herding dogs – the German shepherds, the collies, the sheepdogs and the Pembroke corgis – and reached the grand final. She had to compete with the winning terriers, hounds, gundogs, toy dogs and all the others. She and her owner had to run round the huge ring. Everyone cheered and clapped. She didn't win the whole of Crufts, but it was the very first time that a Cardigan corgi had reached the grand final. I glowed with pride. More and more people would know what we were – not a cross between a collie and a dachshund, but a special, very rare breed of our own. I hope the Queen was watching!

I told Edward how we had met the Swedish vallhunds and the Pembroke corgis. I told him how Pembroke corgis hadn't been able to have tails for seventy-five years because of knocking over Queen Mary's sherry glass. Edward, who is so wise because he listens to the radio all day, told me that was nonsense. It wasn't a glass of sherry; it was a very fine bone china teacup full of the best Earl Grey tea. So there!

22

Farming's the Life

Life for a golfing Cardigan corgi is idyllic. Yes, Crufts was exciting but give me a football and squirrels to chase any day. And it took me quite a time to get over the disappointment of discovering that the Queen has Pembroke and not Cardigan corgis.

I spent two weeks at Miss Ingrid's School of Correction while my owner went on holiday. I lived in the big kennel and had training with the whistle every day. When my owner collected me, Miss Ingrid said I was bombproof. We don't get a lot of bombs in Cambridge but my owner seemed pleased.

My training meant I was soon able to play golf with my owner, off the lead. I sat just in the right place while she hit the ball and I watched it intently but never moved. I ran off exploring and returned to her on the whistle and sat while she hit another shot. I sat still when we got to the green and we both thought I was perfect. I never pooped on the fairway but always under trees. I did chase squirrels but learnt that they climb trees and I can't catch them.

Other golfers would shout across, 'Does she find the ball?' But of course I wouldn't because I have been trained never to touch a ball. Yes, I soon became a five-star golfing dog.

Then I realised that my owner would play golf with other people, not just with me. That came as a bit of a shock. When my owner hit the ball, I stayed beautifully still and completely quiet. The first time I went out with her in a match was a bit of a disaster. I sat still and quiet while she hit the ball but then wriggled and woofed while her opponent hit. Soon I was back on the lead attached to the golf bag for bad behaviour. It was quite distressing.

My owner is quite a famous golfer, even though not as famous as *the* Annika. A man came to write an article about her for a national newspaper. He came with a photographer. They took pictures of my owner playing golf. She said she hoped they didn't mind if I came too. Well, the photographer fell in love with me. I became the star of the newspaper article.

Edward doesn't wear a lead for golf

Stand still, be quiet. I know!

I was so proud when the photos of us appeared in the national magazine. There was a huge picture of me, right up close to the camera, with my owner just a little dot in the distance. Lots of Cardigan corgi owners saw the article. The next time I went to a show I felt quite important, but Edward, in his usual sarcastic way, pointed out that there was actually a chapter called 'Edward the Golfing Cat' in an important golf book. I didn't believe him but then checked it out and found to my dismay that it was absolutely true.

I did really well at the next show, walking beautifully on the mat, standing with my feet just the right width apart and puffing out my chest. Mum Maggie was there and gave me a few tips from the sidelines. She reminded me what to do. I won a rosette for second place.

Although having such exceptionally acute hearing can be an advantage, on this occasion it wasn't so good. I heard the judge talking about my owner and me. She might have thought she was whispering but my ears picked up every word: 'Nice dog, shame about the handler.'

Well, I was mortified. My poor owner was only a beginner at this. Although Mum Maggie could give me coaching from the sidelines, no one is allowed to coach handlers while they're on parade. Unfortunately, my owner had also heard the judge's comments. From that day on, she never dared handle me again in the ring. It was quite demoralising.

We had our first trip to my spiritual home in Wales. We stayed on a lovely sheep farm with my owner's cousin, whose husband farms sheep right on the edge of Snowdon Mountain.

'How is Annika with sheep?' they asked. My owner said that she thought I was fully trained and wouldn't touch them. Of course I wouldn't. So off we went for a tour round the farm, with my owner balanced precariously on the back of a quad bike. I hoped she wouldn't fall off; she did look frightened. I followed on with the five farm dogs – three Welsh collies and two Jack Russells. It was really good fun. We went through ditches, rolled in cow pats, found some duck muck to play in, listened for moles and played ball with sheep poops. None of us took any notice of the sheep. The collies held them back okay while we opened and closed gates. What an adventure!

When we got back to the farmhouse kitchen, we all shared big bowls of tripe and onions and other farmhouse scraps. My owner and her cousin were enjoying tea and I was left to play with the farm dogs. What a life they have.

Loads of chickens were loose in the yard, and I wanted to try my herding skills, so Jack, one of the Jack Russells, helped me herd all the hens into the barn. The silly things fluttered and flapped but we had them well under control. Then, having got them all in, we decided to get them all out again, and herded them out into the yard. One flapped and fluttered and ran under a tractor. Jack stood on one side and I stood on the other side but it escaped, squawking, through the front wheels. We started with ten chickens and now there seemed to be nine. The first rule of herding is to do a head count and make sure you don't lose any. Jack and I had failed completely. We hunted out the chicken and found it, but we could never get all ten in the same place and eventually gave up.

I found an egg. I'd had plenty of training carrying eggs at home and now I'd found one. I carried it slowly and steadily in my mouth, hoping my owner would come and tap it on the side of the bowl so that I could eat it. But Jack had some really good advice.

'What are you doing carrying the egg round like that. Drop it on the concrete over here and see how it breaks. Then we can both share it.' I thought this was probably really naughty but did what Jack said because he was the host. Sure enough, the egg broke and Jack and I had a real feast from it.

'Annika, can you find another one? My teeth are so sharp that if I find one it breaks immediately and gets lost in the straw.'

So off we went, Jack and I, and sure enough found another egg in the straw. I carried that one out as gently as anything, with Jack yapping beside me a little drop-it-on-the-concrete woof. So I did and we enjoyed that one, too.

He showed me round the farmyard. The ducks lived in a pen and we couldn't get at them. It was frustrating to see lovely duck muck inside the pen and have nothing to roll in. Duck muck is very good for a dog's complexion. But Jack showed me where we might find some and we rolled and played in the mud and the dirt. It started to rain and we clambered down into a ditch. I looked down at my paws and they were completely black. In fact, there was nothing white left on me at all except a little bit of white on my nose and the very tip of my tail.

I was off to the dog show the next day and my owner didn't seem too pleased that I was now completely black. I had to be hosed down in the farmyard. Her cousin's husband filled the

This is very undignified

wheelbarrow full of water and I was scrubbed from top to tail. The next morning, after a huge farmhouse breakfast, we went off to the show. All the others had been staying in hotels or caravans. I was the only one who had experienced the proper farm life of the Welsh Cardigan corgi.

Mum Maggie asked why I smelt. My brother, Bryn, the one who is a proper Welsh farm dog, was there. He's a beautiful blue merle – though not as handsome as Ace of course – and he smelt, too. I know now that it isn't rude to sniff your acquaintances and say if they pong a bit, because my owner had said how nice the Frenchman smelt at Crufts.

My owner was too nervous to handle me herself, after the previous judge's comments, so a kind man, Jeff, took me into the ring. This time, since I smelt of duck muck and my feet

Hoorah! It's my brother Bryn

were still a bit stained, the judge's comment was more likely to be, 'Nice handler, shame about the dog.' Mum Maggie said I should be ashamed of myself turning up like that. Jeff wore a smart blue blazer. His aftershave didn't smell quite as nice as that of the gorgeous Frenchman at Crufts, but at least it was enough to hide the smell of duck muck, and we won a nice rosette.

I thought it would be fun to be a Welsh farm dog and have chickens and sheep to look after. Certainly it was more fun than being a show dog.

Through the season we went to lots of exciting places. My owner played golf at Sunningdale, which she says is the smartest golf course in the whole of England. It was a match, so I couldn't play with her, but another lady walked me round the course. My owner gave her £1 to get a special dog lunch. The lady thought it was a joke, but it wasn't. At a really nice cabin halfway round the golf course, where they sell refreshments, she handed over the £1 and in return received lots of change and a receipt that said 'One dog', and I got a couple of cold sausages from the day before. Almost all the golfers had dogs. There were Labradors and retrievers and a couple of dachshunds – Fritz and Heinrich. When they asked me my name and I said it was Annika, they all chuckled with a little we-know-who-you-are-named-after woof.

On the way home we went past Windsor Castle. I told Edward when we got back and he asked whether a large red-and-yellow flag had been flying over the castle. I remembered seeing it and he said it was called the Royal Standard and they fly it whenever the Queen's corgis are there. Edward is such a wise cat and I'm sure he's quite correct. The corgis might be at Buckingham Palace or Windsor Castle or Sandringham or Balmoral up in Scotland. Wherever the corgis go, the special flag is hoisted. I thought that was bit pretentious and asked Edward if he knew whether the Queen had a special flag, too. He said he didn't think so, but wherever the corgis were, the Queen was sure to be.

I asked Edward if the Queen also had cats. He said that cats were banned from royal palaces other than to catch mice. Queen Victoria had a cat and it had a fight with one of her dogs. The dog died. Queen Victoria said, 'We are not amused.'

Edward reminded me that his is a very important royal name. Annika might be important in golf but more British kings had been called Edward than anything else. There have been eight in all compared with six Georges, two Charles and a few Williams. He certainly knows his stuff. Sophie whispered, 'Henry the Eighth', as she hid behind her tail.

Queen Victoria had been given a Cardigan corgi. But one of the servants dressed it in a very thick woolly jacket and pretended it was a Skye terrier. As Edward said, if you look at the picture, it's very obvious. A Skye terrier is just a Cardigan corgi wearing a very thick woolly coat because of the bad weather in the Highlands.

I thought of Sandy, my Skye terrier friend. Edward, of course, was absolutely right. He *is* just a Cardigan corgi wearing an extremely thick, woolly overcoat. I'll remember to check that next time I meet him up in Scotland.

23

Ditto Comes to Stay

Whenever my owner went on holiday, I went to stay with Mrs Cole and Mum Maggie and Ace. I grew to love him more and more and Mum said we would make a great couple and have lovely puppies when the time was right. He was so good-looking and very attentive. Then my owner and Mrs Cole decided we should wait perhaps another year.

The good news, and I suppose it was good news, was that my brother Toby, who, apparently, is very handsome and looks just like me, had had his wicked way with Ace's sister, Bumble, who looks just like him. They had a litter of six puppies, three looking just like Bumble and three looking like Toby. They were my nieces and nephews.

My owner went to visit them at Bumble's house when they were just a few days old. And then she went to visit them again and then I went to visit them when they were about six weeks old. They were quite cute. I wasn't sure I would want puppies of my own, though, what with all that feeding them and washing them and burying their poops under newspaper.

And then my owner arrived home with one of them, Ditto, a blue merle. All black and white and grey speckled. She had come on a holiday, I supposed, presumably to give Bumble a rest.

Ditto our new guest

I knew Ditto wouldn't be a show dog or much good. Firstly, her ears were completely flopped down and she didn't look like a corgi at all. Secondly, she had enormous feet, and thirdly, she has one brown eye and one blue eye. The gardener had made a special pen in the garden for Ditto to play in. I thought my owner was really kind doing this just for Ditto to come on holiday. I didn't know how long she was staying. Mrs Cole came to visit and showed my owner how to do lots of training with Ditto. I assumed that this was so that she would be good enough to sell to new owners. We had special little wooden blocks on the grass for Ditto to stand on. Perhaps her legs were too short – not long and athletic like mine! And every morning my owner had to practise standing Ditto on the kitchen table.

I tried to do my bit by washing her and making her ears stick up. But they wouldn't. I thought this was a bit sad. I knew

Now we have to be in prison

Ditto on stilts – ho, ho!

she would be a reject if she had floppy ears and nobody would want her.

I soon decided it wasn't very nice having a puppy around the house. I had to share my bed and share my chews and she kept wanting to sit where I wanted to sit. The only good thing was that if anything bad happened, I could always blame it on Ditto. I tried my luck. I pulled the Delia Smith cookery book off the bookshelf and ate the front cover. When my owner looked at it, I gave a little it's-Ditto-what-done-it woof. I thought if I did naughty things and blamed her, she would get sent away pretty quickly. I even did a little piddle on the back door mat. It was difficult to make the piddle just small enough so my owner would think it was Ditto's and not mine. That's what my owner did think and I gave another little it's-Ditto-what-done-it woof.

To make matters worse, she got into my very large water bowl in the garden and started trying to swim in it. There was water all over the place and this time my it's-Ditto-what-done-it woof was nothing but the truth.

Ditto seemed to be staying an awful long time. Eventually, one morning I managed to get one of her ears to stand up. Mrs Cole came to visit and held Ditto upside down to see what she would look like with two straight ears rather than floppy ears. I thought Mrs Cole was going to take Ditto home. But she didn't. In fact, she brought another lead with her for Ditto to practise with. And then my owner bought another bed and brought that into the kitchen to put alongside my bed. I continued to do a few odd naughty things, hoping that my owner would send Ditto away. I chewed the end off the red plastic watering can, chewed a couple of plastic bottles, spread

She is in my water bowl!

I thought she was just a visitor

some plastic clothes pegs out on the grass and dug up a few little plants. Whenever my owner looked, I always gave the same it's-Ditto-what-done-it woof. But nothing I said would persuade anyone to send Ditto away.

It was quite difficult sharing my toys with her. She chewed the nose off my beloved red-and-white mouse, ate the tail off my woolly monkey and dug the squeaker out of my furry pheasant. She pushed me out of my bed and wee-weed on my favourite sheepskin rug.

People kept coming to the house and showing far more interest in Ditto than in me. Isn't she cute; isn't she sweet; hasn't she got big paws; isn't she a lovely colour. I suppose it's like that for children when a new baby arrives in their family. I still hoped she was going to go, or it was all just a bad dream. And then Mrs Cole visited with Mum Maggie and Ace. I had almost gone off Ace by this time. Although I had been in love with him so much, he now reminded me of a large version of Ditto. All black and grey and white and spotty. And then Mum Maggie, who is of course Ditto's grandmother, confided in me.

Ditto is coming to live here! This is so unfair

'You know Ditto is probably going to be a very special champion. Everything about her is just right. And she moves so beautifully.'

'You mean with that silly floppy ear Ditto is going to be a champion?' I was horrified. 'But presumably she's going to be someone else's champion. She isn't staying here is she?'

Mum Maggie explained that Ditto would be staying here and coming to live with me. And then I heard Mrs Cole confirm it to my owner.

'Yes, we knew from about three weeks old that everything about Ditto is spot on. She has wonderful bone structure and even at this very early age you can tell she is something special. Maggie was my once in a lifetime dog and Ditto is going to be just the same, I'm sure.'

And there I was, just sitting in the corner, looking at my squeaky ball and hoping someone would play with me.

And there they all were, even Ace, looking at Darling, Delectable, Delicious, aDorable, Desirable – Demanding, Destructive, Dreadful Ditto.

She was coming to live with me and share my life. My little heart was completely broken.

24

Remember Me Too!

My life changed an awful lot once Ditto arrived. And I do mean awful. I couldn't play all the way round the golf course because Ditto couldn't play. I couldn't have the run of the whole house because Ditto couldn't have the run of the whole house. I tried to get her into trouble with my owner by doing naughty things and blaming Ditto, giving my it's-Ditto-what-done-it woof. But my owner and Ditto both got cute to this. Ditto soon learnt an it's-Annika-what-done-it woof.

I started out being kind and sweet to Ditto. I knew how difficult it was to learn to go upstairs and downstairs and tried to show her. But then Sophie got in the way halfway up or halfway down, so I gave up. The advantage was that I had the whole of the upstairs of the house to myself; my little sanctuary.

The ears on a Cardigan corgi are really quite a feature. They are much larger than Pembroke corgis' ears and they are very important for good hearing. I helped Ditto to get her second ear up by licking and playing with it. Eventually, both her ears stood up and I could see that she would be a Cardigan corgi after all. But when she started pulling at my ears, well that was quite enough.

She was going to be a show dog, so her training was completely different from mine. Show dogs don't sit; they

Ditto with one ear up

stand. Show dogs don't cuddle up beside their owner's left leg; they stride out in front, looking important. I couldn't help Ditto with any of this. She copied me when we waited for the back gate to be opened, though. We were never allowed through before our owner – I would sit and Ditto had to stand. And when she had training to return to the whistle, I explained it to her. 'Two blasts of the whistle and we rush back to our owner.' That was a disaster. The little creature was so stupid that immediately the whistle went she'd run like the clappers. She wouldn't deviate for a squirrel, or sniff anything on the way, and so would always get there first.

'Isn't Ditto wonderful?' my owner would say. I must remember it's our owner. Oh hell!

My owner decided to train Ditto not to touch a golf ball, but there was no chance of that anyway. She wouldn't touch a golf ball, she wouldn't touch or run for a squeaky ball, she wouldn't play football. She would just strut round the garden, looking important. I warned her about Edward and Sophie but she had no inclination to chase cats, just as she had no inclination to chase squirrels or balls or anything else. She was just Miss Perfect.

When she arrived, as a very small puppy, she annoyed me by sitting in my big water bowl. When she got older my owner – our owner – bought her a shallow, pink bucket, which she used as a paddling pool. Perhaps water was going to be her weakness and I could drown her.

Still more visitors came to 'ooh' and 'aah' over Delectable, Delicious, Delightful Ditto. My owner had spent hours photographing me, but now she photographed Ditto – Ditto

My new sports equipment

in the paddling pool, Ditto yawning, Ditto on her front, Ditto on her back. Photograph me, please, like you used to do.

I became quite a forlorn creature. Our owner – there, I got it right that time – bought me some agility equipment. I had posts to weave around, hoops to jump through, a stiff tunnel and a floppy tunnel. I had a ramp with a bar to walk along

Trying to help her ears stand up!

War games

and a seesaw. I was back in control because there was no way Ditto was going to be allowed to use that. Edward was more of a problem. He sat on the top of my boardwalk and stopped me using it. He stared at me from the other end of my tunnel so that I couldn't go through. He rubbed himself up and down against my weaving posts and sprayed on my hoops. But at least Ditto showed no signs of athleticism or inclination towards agility.

I decided the best use for Ditto was to practise herding with her. I chased her round the garden this way and that, just as though she was a naughty sheep. Something went a bit wrong and I finished up with a load of her white fur in my mouth. That was the best game, herding Ditto and then rolling her over and jumping on her. I discovered how to pin her down. As she grew bigger, it became more difficult. But I could turn her on her back, stand over her, and put my paws on her ears.

Now she's got ears!

It's wonderful to have someone to blame

But I got worried that she was going to grow bigger than I am, and might retaliate.

Every day she had her show-dog training. She would stand still on the four blocks; they were put farther and farther apart as she got longer. Our owner would stand her on the kitchen worktop, practising for shows. Ditto was so perfect that she would never try to creep along the worktop and steal gravy or cheese. She just stood there on her own.

She so loved being on tables that if a chair was ever left in the wrong place she would climb up on to the kitchen table and just stay there. Getting up was all right but she hadn't learnt how to get down. Our owner would often return to the house to find me minding my own business in my bed and Ditto standing helplessly on the kitchen table.

Oh Perfect One!!

One day our owner did get Ditto to the top of the stairs. We both explained to Ditto that stairs are dangerous and that she must wait until our owner shouts 'all right', which was the sign to run down again. One day, while our owner was out, Ditto got to the top of the stairs and because there was no one to shout 'all right', she just sat there.

About the same time that Ditto arrived, Barney's owner got a new playmate for him, Lucca. Edward, who is, of course, very wise, said that Lucca was mentioned in the first chapter of *War and Peace*. He thought Lucca was a town in Italy, but that sounded very unlikely.

Lucca is a Labradoodle. That's a cross between a Labrador and a poodle. Edward said that Lucca would be very intelligent

Barney's new housemate, Lucca

indeed. The good looks would come from the Labrador but the intelligence would come from the poodle. Edward pointed out that the name 'poodle' comes from 'puddlehund' and that Lucca would love water. I thought this was a bit far-fetched but Edward is full of wise words. Barney confided in me that he also found it difficult to have a new, young playmate. Lucca pinched his teddy bear and tried to sit in Barney's favourite place on the sofa. Lucca, unlike Ditto, was not going to be a show dog. Labradoodles don't get shown. So he learnt to sit down and wait and come to the whistle. He would have been much more fun to sit down and play with than Ditto. Like me, Lucca was totally obsessed with playing with a ball. Unfortunately, he became just that bit quicker than I am and would often get to the ball a moment before I did. But he was the perfect gentleman and would always leave the ball for me, particularly if I threatened to bite him on the ankles!

Lucca and Ditto would play for hours. They were both obsessed with water. Whenever they found water – a puddle, a fishpond, a stream, a pond or a lake – Ditto and Lucca were in it. Perhaps Edward was right about the puddlehund. I could see the possible departure of Ditto being played out before me. Damp, Dripping, Dreadfully Drowned Ditto.

25

Seaside Holidays

We all went on holiday to Eastbourne. That's Barney and Lucca and their owner, and Ditto, my owner and me. Edward and Sophie stayed at home because cats don't travel. We played on the very stony beach but it was wonderful. Our owners would fling tennis balls and squeaky balls and Barney, Lucca and I would chase after them and retrieve them. Barney has a silly habit of picking up the ball and dropping it in the sea but Lucca would swim and collect it and bring it back. I liked to paddle at the edge of the water but no more than that; no more than getting my paws wet and certainly not swimming.

Finders, keepers

Now who looks like a star?

As usual, Ditto showed no interest in any of the balls. She found crabs and shells to play with, and stole some lugworms from a bucket, which were a fisherman's bait. Fortunately, he didn't notice. I tried to give a watch-your-lugworms woof. I hoped she might be arrested for stealing but no such luck. Ditto barked at the waves and had great fun jumping over the breakwaters and then running back underneath them.

She did the funniest thing. She found a stone, dug a hole beside it and kept shouting at the stone to fall in the hole. Then she made the hole larger and larger and farther away from the stone, but it wouldn't fall in. Why do silly puppies do that? Mum Maggie says it's quite common – quite daft!

I loved being at the seaside. The wind was blowing strongly along the beach and walking into it was very hard going. The ball wouldn't travel anywhere. Our owner kicked my football back the way we had come, so the wind was behind it. Off it went, dancing and bouncing, rushing ahead of me with a mind of its own. I should think it went almost a mile and I chased it all the way. It eventually stopped and snuggled up against a breakwater. I nosed it out and started to take it back to the others. I pushed it with my nose and prodded it with my paws but it was hard work against the wind. So I decided

Born to play ball

244

I can try my herding skills on Barney

to pick it up, but when I grabbed it with my teeth, I heard a gushing, rushing noise and the football whistled at me. It was soon much easier to get my teeth into. I ran with it for a little way and then dropped it. I put my paw on it and it was all limp and floppy, not a ball at all. The ball was spluttering and coughing and I thought it best to leave it to die in peace beside a washed-up plastic milk bottle. When I got back to the others, our owner simply shouted, 'Oh Annika, you've popped your favourite football. Yes, it must be a basketball in future.'

Barney and I went on a boat ride and the two little ones had to stay behind. That made me feel important. Perhaps my owner did love me after all. Barney said he felt the same way. Having new youngsters in a household isn't easy. The boat trip was great. Barney was a bit of a wimp getting in and out of the boat, even though his legs are much longer than mine. He is a bit of a mummy's boy and an attention seeker.

We went to a café, while the little ones were still in the car, and sat outside. Barney and I sat under the table, and it's a wonder I don't have an inferiority complex. Everyone who came along looked at Barney and said, 'Oh what a beautiful golden retriever. How old is he? Isn't he handsome? What's his name?' I might as well have been a well-worn handbag or an old coat thrown under the table for all the attention I got. Even my owner was a bit miffed that nobody noticed me. And then, joy of joys, a man and woman with two small children came by and spotted ME.

'Oh my goodness. Is that a corgi? I've never seen a corgi that colour. She's a Cardigan corgi? That's not the ones the Queen has. They're the Pembroke corgi. How interesting. This one is so much larger and prettier, and what a gorgeous tail. Would it be all right for the children to stroke her?' I was in seventh heaven. The children crouched down close beside me and I remembered about letting them stroke my ears and kissing them.

'Thank you so much for letting us meet your little corgi.'

Barney was put out and said he might just as well have been an old pair of trainers or yesterday's newspaper under the table for all they cared. I told him that was how I usually felt when everyone fussed over him. And Barney's owner was equally irritated. She snatched the bill and went off inside to pay it as an act of defiance.

We went back to the seashore again at low tide. Like all responsible dog owners, ours had a supply of poop bags for scooping up any whoopsies. Ditto managed to do hers right in the edge of the sea so our owner was left chasing after it. I thought I would do the same, because it seemed clean and tidy.

And then a man shouted, 'Do you know your corgi has pooped in the sea?'

'No,' said our owner. 'You hum it and I'll play it!'

I didn't really know what she meant but they all laughed, including the man, and they chased my whoopsie with a poop bag.

When it was 'Ditto what done it', my owner had laughed. When it was 'Annika what done it', my owner was cross, and I was left feeling insecure and unloved. Barney told me not to

Look at me please!

be silly. That was easy for him to say because everyone loves a golden retriever.

Barney and Lucca were swimming around in the sea. Barney's owner threw stones for him and he swam to the centre of the splash, even though there was nothing to retrieve. Lucca would swim after the tennis ball and bring it right back to her. And then I could see that Ditto was swimming. Her legs aren't very long – not as long as mine – and she was clearly out of her depth, swimming along, round and round, back and forwards.

'Oh look everyone. Ditto's swimming. Hurrah! Isn't she clever? Look at her go! Isn't she brilliant?'

I was just sitting there. I might as well have been a piece of driftwood, a dead fish or a washed-up tin can for all anyone cared about me. Swim? You want to see a corgi swim? I hated the idea of swimming. I didn't want to get my tummy wet and certainly didn't want to get water in my eyes or ears. But if she could do it, I could do it.

I paddled into the water and could feel the wet sand and grit between my toes. I went out farther and farther until eventually my paws were off the ground. Head down, tail out, I just kept paddling away. Back on the seashore I could hear my owner shouting, 'Oh my goodness look at Annika. She's swimming. Annika, come back.'

But I just kept on swimming. It was my first adventure in the water and I could only do straight lines. I had no idea how to swim round in a curve or return to the seashore. I just kept on swimming and heard them shouting, 'You'll have to go after her. She'll finish up in France.'

'That'll show them,' I thought. 'I'll just keep going. I don't know where France is but I'm sure someone will come and fetch me.'

'Annika, come back.'

I will swim right out to France and see if she comes to get me

But I just had thoughts of France in my mind and kept on paddling. Eventually, after several minutes, my feet touched some sand again. I found myself standing on a huge stretch of sand, all alone apart from a few seagulls.

'Wait there, Annika, I'm coming to get you.' And there was my owner, swimming out towards me, wearing her shirt and shorts, and eventually wading out to me and standing on the sand beside me.

I wasn't sure whether I had actually reached France. I didn't know anything about France except that Frenchmen supposedly smell very nice. But there weren't any men, just seagulls. My owner had brought the rope lead with her and she put it round my neck. First she waded while I swam beside her and then we both had to swim. And then, eventually, she could get her feet on the ground and soon I could, too. I was rescued. I looked back at the stretch of sand where I had been standing to see it rapidly disappearing under water.

A man shouted, 'If that ever happens again, call the Coastguards. They'll always come out to rescue a dog or owner in trouble.'

Another man who had been swimming lent a towel to dry me and a fisherman gave me a piece of his beefburger from his picnic bag. My owner was crying with tears of relief that I had been rescued. Ditto was just playing with a crab and showing no interest. I realised that my owner did love me after all. I suppose that she had risked her life to save mine. What more could a little corgi ask for?

26

Damnable Ditto

After the Eastbourne adventure, I began to see Ditto in a new light. She was never going to replace me but she was here to stay, so I'd better get used to it and outsmart her. We went to a very big dog show in London – one of those shows where every breed has a stand and chosen Cardigan corgis stand on the table, kiss the children and have their photos taken. The people on the Cardigan corgi stand were so thrilled to see me. This is the very best part of the job of a Welsh Cardigan corgi. My public was there, awaiting me. Ditto, who was only just six months old by then, spent most of the time in the pen, yawning a lot.

A national dog magazine had run a special competition to guess the breed of dog and the picture was of Ditto, as a small puppy, with floppy ears and shaking her head from side to side, so that it was blurred. Thousands of people had entered the competition but only three had guessed she was a Cardigan corgi. Our owner took us over to the award stand, ready for the announcement of the winner. As we walked through the hall, people kept stopping and wanting to talk to our owner about Ditto. A man, whom Edward said later he thought must have been Russian, offered our owner ten thousand pounds for Ditto. I thought she should have accepted it and we could have had a new sports car. But she didn't.

The man from the dog magazine announced the winner of the 'Guess the Breed' competition, saying, 'Yes, everyone, it's a Cardigan corgi. And here she is. It's Ditto our Cardigan corgi.'

And all the spectators said, 'Ooh,' and, 'Aah,' and several people said they didn't know there were such things as

Picture competition – I mustn't be envious of the Little Treasure!

Cardigan corgis. I tried to make them look at me with a little I'm-a-Cardigan-corgi-too woof. But no one was very interested. So I did a little wee to remind my owner that I was there, and gave a little it's-Ditto-what-done-it woof. But she wasn't interested. No one was interested.

Ditto stood on the countertop to have her photo taken with the lucky winner and everyone cheered, but she woofed to me, 'Annika, help me. Why have these people won me as a prize? I want to come home with you, Annika.'

Poor Ditto. The life of a champion and a little film star might not be much fun after all. I suddenly didn't mind that everybody loved Ditto. I didn't mind that she was going to be a champion and I wasn't. I remembered the nasty class that frightened me so much – the dog the judge would most like to take home. Now poor Ditto thought she had been won as a prize. I reassured her that we were all going home together. She was overjoyed.

I now knew that I must accept and support Darling Ditto in everything she did. Our skills are very different. And, after all, my owner had swum, fully clothed, complete with her wristwatch, out into the sea to rescue me. I understood then that having two dogs doesn't mean that love is halved. It just means that love is shared.

I was learning to glow with pride at Ditto's successes, and I really tried not to be envious of her. She had her role to play as a show dog while I was the games player. I was the one with the football, the squeaky balls, the agility set and, of course, the love of golf.

We went to loads of shows and Ditto won nearly everything she was entered for. Our owner pinned all our rosettes on the curtains in the kitchen. I had one pair of curtains at one end of the kitchen, and Ditto had the curtains at the other end. I had lots of rosettes, red ones and blue ones and yellow ones. And I had one enormous rosette with five rings of green and yellow and great long tassels. It had the word 'Congratulations' written on it. Everyone thought I must have done something very special, but in reality our owner had won it for an important dog photography competition. Ditto's rosettes were nearly all red for first places with plenty of special ones saying 'Best Puppy', 'Best Bitch' and 'Best of Breed'.

Truth to tell, I was still a bit fed up with all the attention Ditto was receiving. And gradually there looked to be more rosettes on her pair of curtains than there were on mine. I didn't exactly try to scupper her show career, but I thought I might make it a little more difficult.

There are some lovely muddy places on our golf course, and I know exactly the best spots for rolling in duck muck and fox poop. And then the molehills are fun to roll around and bunkers are great to play in. The best combination for getting really filthy is to start by going in one of the ponds that's surrounded by black, dirty mud, and then rolling in duck poop or on molehills or in bunkers, so that all the dirt sticks to the nice, wet fur. I taught Ditto all about doing this and she was first class at it. It meant we had to be taken back into the garden and hosed down and sometimes taken upstairs and dumped in a bath and cleaned off. I remembered what had happened to me at the Welsh show when I had to be dunked in a wheelbarrow.

I always knew when we were due to go to shows. Our owner would trim up our toenails and get out the buzz-buzz to get them really short. This was a sure sign to me that I should get Ditto filthy and in trouble. I'm sure the other dogs that were being shown were having special treatment in their homes and were probably not allowed out at all. I have to say, though, that Ditto was born to be a show dog. She was trained from a very early age to love the hairdryer and she will stand on the table while her fur is blasted with a special air gun. Still, it was fun trying.

My full pedigree, with all my champion ancestors marked in red, was framed and hung on the wall. It took pride of place next to a certificate for our owner, signed by the Queen and

She can get up . . . but can't get down!

Big Ears!

Prince Philip. That always made me feel so special. Ditto's much smaller version of her pedigree, which was black and white and not coloured, hung in the downstairs toilet. I knew that she was really second place to me, whatever her future.

We went to Wales for the championships, and Ditto even went to Ireland with Mrs Cole while I stayed at home to play golf with our owner. After Ditto's trip to Ireland she received two special certificates of green stars. I didn't know what they were for but they must have been important because they were framed and hung beside her pedigree in the downstairs toilet.

Still, I glowed with pride that it was my pedigree that hung in a frame beside my owner's certificate from the Queen.

We went to Edinburgh for the Scottish championships. I hoped so much that we might call in at Newcastle on the way for my footballing dream. We passed the Angel of the North, which is a huge sculpture, marking the entrance to Newcastle.

I pointed it out to Ditto and said how much it looked like our owner's shadow, which I had erroneously thought was a dragon. But Ditto wasn't interested and doesn't, of course, share my passion for football.

Despite Miss Ingrid's words of wisdom at her School of Correction, my owner was still carrying on conversations with Sidney Satnav and with me. She did remark that we had reached Newcastle and asked Sidney, 'Is that the football stadium?' But we didn't visit it, either on the way up or on the way down.

The Scottish show was held in enormous marquees. The weather was too bad for us to be in show rings outside. There was plenty of time to meet the other competitors. We found the Skye terriers, and there was my old acquaintance Sandy. It was a relief to him and to me that his owner was wearing trousers and not a kilt on such a very windy day. I introduced

No, Ditto – Sandy is not *a Cardigan corgi in a thick, woollen coat*

him to Ditto. She embarrassed me so much when she repeated Edward's words about Skye terriers.

'Are you sure you're not just a Cardigan corgi wearing a very thick, woolly, furry overcoat?' she asked him.

Sandy wasn't amused and said that when women make inane comments like this, it justifies why men in Scotland don't want them on golf courses. We made our peace with Sandy. It was no good chastising Ditto and upsetting her before the show.

It was just so windy that it sounded like the whole marquee was going to blow over, but Ditto and I are both trained to deal with bad weather. We know all about marquees because we have one at the golf club. I was completely bombproof and Ditto just copied me. We won lots of rosettes and our owner was happy. Ditto even won a special certificate and Mrs Cole said that Ditto was now qualified to compete at Crufts for life, just like my Mum Maggie – Ditto's grandmother.

Meanwhile, my own show career had been blossoming. We had both qualified for Crufts. Ditto qualified as Special Puppy for little ones up to fifteen months and I was qualified in Post Graduate and Good Citizen class. My class of Post Graduate is really for the third level. There is the Open class for the real champions, Limit for dogs who are very nearly champions and Post Graduate for newcomers. In golfing terms, I heard my owner say, I was Silver Division B – whatever that meant.

Jeff, my special handler, was there to take me in the ring at Crufts. My owner hadn't got over hearing that judge say, 'Nice dog, shame about the handler.' Jeff got me all spruced up and spick and span. Ditto had won the Special Puppy class, with Mrs

Cole in attendance. I expect it was a foregone conclusion. In our class, lots of girls were hoping for success. It was a lovely big ring. That's where my athleticism came into play. For some of the girls it was a long way round and some of them had elderly handlers, who were puffing and panting to go so far. But Jeff, wearing his lovely dark, cherry coloured blazer, led me in and we glided round that show ring like Fred Astaire and Ginger Rogers. I stood on the table and thought of all the practice Ditto had done. Jeff set my feet correctly, with my front paws just wide enough apart. I tried to puff out my chest like Dolly Parton and I looked adoringly at Jeff and then at the judge. We did a triangle, up to the end of the ring and back again, and I looked adoringly at the judge again, and then stood very, very still.

Guess what – we won! I won an enormous red rosette and was given a big red diamond-shaped card to say I was a winner. Ditto looked really pleased that I had won and gave a well-done-Annika woof. She was pleased for me and I must be pleased for her.

Then came the Good Citizen class for those of us who had obedience awards – I have my silver award. We don't do obedience in the show ring; it goes on looks and behaviour and, guess what, I won that one, too. No, that's selfish. Jeff and I won that one, too. We had another rosette and another lovely red card. Ditto looked pleased for me and proud of me, so I must always be proud of her. I think she knows she will be a champion one day and I realised what a good sport she is.

And then Ditto beat the special boy puppy and so was the best puppy of all. Ditto went back in her cage and was covered over like a parrot to go to sleep. Later, she had photos taken and I knew she was very important. Another man from Russia tried to buy her. This time I protested with a she's-not-for-sale woof. And someone wanted to borrow her to show her for the rest of the season. Before, I wanted my owner to take the money and have a new sports car. Now, I felt protective and quite cross.

My owner and I went for an expedition round the halls. She was to do shopping; I was to do shoplifting. Lots of other owners were walking around with rosettes, red and blue and yellow, pinned on their jackets. My owner had other ideas. My two lovely red rosettes were pinned on my rope lead to show it was my success and not hers. In fact, a lot of the success was down to Jeff because I started to do well and win once he was in charge. My owner bought me another lovely red leather collar with fake diamonds on it. Mrs Cole was horrified and said show dogs shouldn't wear glitzy collars, but my owner reminded her that I'm not really a show dog, just a footballing, golfing dog who gets shown.

Over the next few months, with Jeff in charge, I won five times in the Post Graduate class at big shows. I felt really puffed up and excited after the fifth win because it took me into the Limit class with the nearly champions. I'll probably never win again at that level, so I have achieved all I can in the show ring. Other dogs and owners celebrate when their dogs become champions. We had a celebration because I had done better than ever expected. Mum Maggie was thrilled with my success.

'Now,' I thought, 'it's all down to Ditto and I must support her all the way. Hurrah for Ditto. Hurrah, hurrah.'

27

Ace – Love of My Life

With Ditto firmly on course for a successful show career, thoughts turned to the possibility of my having puppies. I saw Ace from time to time when Ditto and I went to stay with Mum Maggie if our owner was on holiday. I really did adore Ace because he was so handsome. He's big and strong and just a lovely, good-natured boy. Ditto's mum is Ace's sister Bumble – in case you'd forgotten – and Ditto's dad is my brother Toby. So there were great hopes that Ace and I might produce a lovely litter of puppies.

Mrs Cole decided when the time was right for me to stay with Ace and play mummies and daddies. He was lovely and sweet and gentle. We cuddled in the kennel and we cuddled on the sofa and we cuddled in the garden under a hedge and in the sunshine. We cuddled in the little summerhouse and we slept together each night in 'the bridal suite' in the garden. We had so much to talk about. We remembered how we had first met, when I had a bucket on my head, and how he had shocked everyone with the noise of his singing and purring. We cuddled up together but he was such a gentleman and wouldn't do anything naughty at all and certainly not something that was smutty.

After eight days, I went home to our owner and we started

I hoped Ace and I would have lovely puppies of our own!!

planning for the puppies. I knew exactly where they were going to be born and had found a lovely nest under a shrub by our large summerhouse. It was warm and cosy in there and just the right place for puppies. I visited it most days just to make sure no one was going there. I confided in Ditto and Edward that that was where the puppies would be born. Edward had funny ideas that he might pick them off one at a time, like he did with the ducklings. Our owner suspected he might do this, so I think he was booked into the cat kennels for the puppies' first week.

Ditto was trying to work out what relations the puppies would be to her. I explained they would be cousins but it was a little hard for her to grasp. After four weeks I did seem to be getting chubbier and my owner took me to the vet to have me scanned. This would prove how many puppies I was due to have. The vet said I hadn't got puppies at all and my owner sobbed on the way home. But I knew she was wrong and there would be puppies. I knew the exact date when they were coming. There were going to be four of them – three boys and a girl. I wanted them to be Wildcard David Beckham, Wildcard Wayne Rooney, Wildcard Alan Shearer – my Newcastle hero – and a little girl, Wildcard Maggie after Mum. I don't care what the vet thought. There were puppies on the way. I kept checking my nest and just a couple of days before the puppies were due to be born I noticed I was producing milk, ready to feed them.

And then the day came for the puppies to be born. And they weren't born. And the next day they weren't born. And they weren't born the next day, either. They were getting very late and I kept checking the nest. I was worried somebody had

Dreaming of puppies – but they didn't arrive!

taken them in the night while I wasn't looking. It was quite a frantic time. Mrs Cole told my owner that if there had been a litter of puppies needing a mum I could have adopted them. That was stupid because my own ones were going to arrive sometime.

After a week the puppies still hadn't arrived. I felt really depressed and sat in my bed. I gathered up the furry pheasant, the woolly monkey, the cuddly teddy bear and the red-and-

I'll have to make do with these!

white mouse and pretended these were my puppies until the real ones arrived. After another week I had to conclude that the vet was right after all. It was a real disappointment and it took me quite a long time to get over it. I had planned their names and dreamt of their careers and thought about how I would lovingly teach them to go up and down stairs and make their ears stand up and what a proud mum I would be. I would teach them not to eat chocolate, not to touch toads, how to play football and how to listen for moles. Oh, they would have been the loveliest Cardigan corgi puppies in the whole, wide world. Mothering the furry pheasant, the woolly monkey, the cuddly teddy and the red-and-white mouse just wasn't the same. I cuddled more with Ditto and I think she knew it was a sad time for me. I think Ditto really is a treasure – Dear Ditto. No, Dearest Ditto. No, Darling, Dearest Ditto.

Yes, my little heart was broken once again.

But then one day a ball squeaked outside, the postman arrived with biscuits, Ditto climbed on the kitchen table and came face to face with a spitting Edward, and our owner took me out to play football.

Who wanted kids anyway? Woof. Perhaps next time!

28

Family Gossip

Was I pleased not to be having puppies? I'm not sure. It meant that things could get back to normal, and I carried on having lots of fun playing football and golf.

Then, at the next couple of shows, the girls started to talk to me about motherhood. The things we talk about on the benches would amaze our owners. We talk about the judges. There are the ones who tweak your ears too hard, the ones who breathe garlic or whisky at you, and the ones who are kind and always praise us. But we also talk about things at home, families and puppies.

'We thought you were having puppies, Annika.'

'What happened? Ace is so handsome and we thought you would have a litter of real gems.'

'Glad you aren't having that litter. They would have been such competition for the rest of us.'

'You be careful, Annika. If you don't have puppies, your owner will probably sell you and get a new girl.'

I couldn't believe it. Sell me because I didn't have puppies? Then, joy of joys, I went to a show where Mum Maggie was on parade, and I asked her about the puppies.

'Don't worry, Annika,' she told me. 'There will be other opportunities to play mummies and daddies with lovely Ace.

This is much better than having puppies!

And if things didn't work with him, I'm sure we could find you another boyfriend.'

I couldn't believe what I was hearing. Find a new boyfriend? Certainly not. I told Mum Maggie what the girls had said. Would my owner really sell me, or give me away, if I didn't have puppies? She reassured me that this was totally unlikely.

'Your owner wants you as a companion, not to have puppies. If you and Ace have a litter, that will just be a bonus for everyone. But your owner wants you for the love you give, your lovely ears, the way you play ball better than any other corgi in the whole world, and your patience and kindness to Ditto.'

I didn't dare tell Mum that I was still a little envious of Delicious, Delightful, Desirable, Demanding, Dreadful Ditto

I had eaten Ditto's best rosette!

and had tried to drown her in my water bowl. I didn't tell Mum I had eaten Ditto's poshest rosette and bitten off its tails.

'You see, Annika, having a litter of puppies isn't the thrill you probably imagine. First of all, you have to carry these new puppies in your tummy as they grow. You will get fatter and fatter and not be able to play golf or football. It takes a whole nine weeks for the puppies to grow. They start kicking and you can feel them. Kick, kick. And then you have to eat special food to make sure they grow big and strong. All that takes nine weeks. You would be kept at home for the last few weeks.

'And then comes the big day when the puppies are born. Owners always stay with you in case they can help. The first litter of puppies I had – your older brothers and sisters – was a real surprise. I didn't know what was happening. When the first puppy plopped out, I thought I'd done something naughty and pushed him under the cooker. Then my owner came to help and heard him squeaking. Out popped the other pups and all was well.'

'It must be very exciting to see the new pups.'

'Well, not really. Puppies are all born blind and are like little rats with pink noses. And the noise – squeaking and squealing and constantly fighting each other to grab a teat for a drink. I've had a couple of really greedy boys. Your brother Bryn was a shocker and I had to keep grabbing Emily and Kiki to get them to feed.'

I discussed the whole subject long and hard with Mum. It seemed that the nine weeks spent carrying the pups was likely to be boring, with no sports and no shows. And then, of course, four weeks or so had to be spent just looking after the little, unattractive, pink-nosed rats.

But what I heard next really shocked me.

'What do you mean? I wouldn't be able to keep them all? But Mum, if I have six lovely puppies, I'm certainly not going to want to give them away at eight weeks.'

I thought that I would be able to keep them all. I was horrified. Mum reminded me about the way my brothers and sisters had all gone to new homes. I knew that, of course, but I thought that was just Mum Maggie's litters. I didn't realise it happened all the time, to everyone.

'Annika, your puppies would be special and would probably go to homes in other countries. Remember how Kiki and Totti went to Finland when they were really tiny. Of course I missed

And Totti has a new girl friend - a lovely Pembroke. But we can't help that!

them. Kiki has become a real star of the dog shows. We always knew she would be a champion. Your brother, Totti, has the happiest of homes. He lives in Helsinki in Finland with his owners and has a special friend, Mona, who is a pretty little Pembroke corgi. They live in the country in the summer and he is like you and loves sports and swimming.

'My owner speaks to their owners on the phone or computer and I woof and bark in the background to exchange our news. These days we can even see each other on the computer. I nudge my owner's elbow and cuddle up close to get in the picture. It's not the same as being with you but at least I know you are all safe and happy. Bryn of course is in Wales on the farm with his sheep and cattle to look after, Toby is in Scotland and then Emily has just moved to Belgium. You would just have to accept that you can't possibly keep your puppies.'

'You mean we spend nine weeks with puppies growing inside us; we look after them and feed them and wash them and pick up their poops and teach them about life – and someone takes them away? I'm not going to put up with that. I'd run away or hide them in the garden. If you think I'm going to waste seventeen weeks producing puppies for other people, you've another think coming.'

Mum was quite shocked, but I knew now – I was *not* going to have puppies.

I heard my owner on the phone. 'No, sadly Annika didn't have puppies. But there'll be other occasions with Ace. And if she doesn't … well, I can just wait for Ditto.'

I decided to be a proud auntie for all the puppies from Toby and Kiki, and perhaps to wait until Ditto could have her puppies. Dearest, Domesticated Ditto!

My niece, Magic, fun but no responsibility!

29

Ditto – the Special One

D itto continued to do marvellously in her shows. I really couldn't understand why my owner didn't sell her. Offers rolled in from people in Europe, and yet another lady wanted, in effect, to rent her for the season, to win with her all over Europe. I'd got over my Crufts feelings of protectiveness and, frankly, I thought it was ridiculous not to take the money. But my owner is quite infatuated with Ditto.

Remember, I'm an athlete

Personally, I can't see it. She can't play ball. She runs around but never tackles me. She can't catch, and if she does get a ball, she doesn't understand about taking it back to our owner. She's horribly perfect on the golf course. She stands absolutely still, to attention, when our owner hits the ball and never runs after it. She just isn't much fun.

And then I found Ditto's weakness – squirrels and ducks. The silly creature just loves chasing squirrels. So do I. But I realise that they rush up trees and you can't catch them. My trick is to hide down the bottom and hope they scamper down into my jaws. Of course, they never do. But Ditto just sits at the bottom of the tree and yells. Our squirrels have her trained. My favourite one, Simon, creeps out along the branch above her head and bounces up and down, up and down. Simon even bounces across from one tree to another and Ditto just sits at the bottom of the wrong tree. She can't understand where he goes!

And as for ducks – Ditto swims after them. They swim round and round. She follows and eventually they fly off. She just doesn't understand.

But as for showing, I have to admit she's a real star. I find showing rather boring and have been known to yawn, but Ditto really lives for being shown. She really is a show-off. Our owner practises with her in the squash court, up and down on the mat and up and down on the table. And I remembered how she had those little blocks to stand on when she was a puppy. That was to train her to keep her feet in the exact position. I just do what comes naturally. But she did do well.

At last Ditto's playing ball

Ditto has a special pink cage with her name on. Usually at shows she stays in her box until it's time to come out. I think that's in case she rolls in something dirty and makes a mess of her fur. I go out straight away. I love shows for the shopping. I have been known to shoplift but always escape arrest or conviction. My favourites are those lovely, smelly dried fish goodies. But I have also snatched a squeaky little pheasant. A man kept pressing the pheasant's tummy and I fancied I could hear the pheasant asking me to rescue him; so I did. Our owner occasionally feels sorry for me and buys me a rosette when all I have won is a certificate. And then we watch while the show goes on. I always used to be in the classes after Ditto. She was in puppy and then junior. I was in one of the adult classes. Now I go in first in the Limit class and Ditto is in with all the stars in the Open class.

Everyone so praises the little creature that it becomes quite tedious. One day it was my turn. I won my class, she won her class, we had a playoff and, hoorah, the judge chose me. Yes, little me. Best Bitch. Best of Breed. I tried to make a very defiant gesture to Ditto. Take that! But the little thing just paddled across to me, flung her paws round me, and kissed my nose and ears. 'Oh, well done, Annika. We all *so* love you.' She's just too good to be true. And when we arrived home she even told Edward that I had won the show. I don't think I'm quite so generous in my praise for her.

She went to a special show with the handler, while I stayed home to play golf. And then the phone call came through.

Stick games

Ditto had won a ticket. I really couldn't contain myself. She came home with a certificate and three huge rosettes.

'Annika, I won the ticket. What does that mean?'

'Ho, ho,' I thought. All that pampering and perfect preparation and performance and she doesn't know what a ticket is. I explained the system to Edward. (It was nice for me to be able to impart wisdom to him for a change.) Tickets are given at very special shows, one for the best girl and one for the best boy. Once a dog has three tickets, he or she becomes a champion and has the letters CH in front of the name. But I wasn't going to let on to Daft Ditto.

'Well, Ditto. Every time you win a ticket you get Air Miles. You save up lots of tickets and eventually you have enough to fly away to another country. Our owner is probably saving up to send you abroad. Three tickets and you become a champion and they put CH in front of your name.'

Ditto was quite sad. 'Me, sent away? I want to stay with you and Edward and Sophie.'

But I just chuckled, and Edward smiled that amusing sort of smile that cats do.

30

Happiness is a Duck Pond

Soon I was taken to visit Ace again for another game of mummies and daddies, and this time I gave him a very good talking to as soon as I arrived.

'Now, it's like this. I've decided I don't want puppies under any circumstances. I'm not going to spend nine weeks carrying them while they grow in my tummy and kick me and another eight weeks looking after the little things. It's all right for you. A corgi orgy and that's it. No responsibilities, no pain. No giving up football for seventeen weeks. So don't get any funny ideas please.

'I had no idea that having puppies meant looking after them, getting attached to them, learning to love them and then having them taken away. Mum Maggie says puppies are such a nuisance, with their chewing and squeaking, that most mums are pleased to see them go. Not me. I was determined to have enough for a little football team.'

Ace and I spent a week together, cuddling on the sofa, cuddling in the kennel and cuddling in the sunshine under the hedge. But every time he tried to have his wicked way with me, I just sat down on the important little piece of me he wanted. It was difficult to get him to take no for an answer. So eventually, I bit him on the nose. He didn't take it terribly well.

Herding Ditto – the special one!

'Annika, if we don't have puppies this time, it will be a reflection on my manhood.'

'That's as may be.'

And that's just what happened. We didn't have puppies and poor Ace was blamed.

My girlfriends at the next show were all very sympathetic. I just pretended that I was disappointed, but in my little heart I was *so* relieved. No puppies. Whoopee! The chatter was all about Ace. Had he? Hadn't he? Was I going to have a new boyfriend?

'You're lucky your owner is going to keep you.'

Of course she would keep me. I am me, Annika, her pride and joy. Her companion, her golfing partner, her best friend.

My owner was nowhere to be seen. I expect she was buying me a new red collar, with diamonds and real silver buckles; and perhaps some of those special dried fish sticks; and a new football. There she is. Here she comes. I can see the new collar. It's blue with gold. I don't have blue. And no football.

'Oh, Annika. My precious one. What a glorious day. At last. I'm so thrilled.'

I pricked up my ears, waggled my whiskers, flicked up my tail, and twitched my nose. What have I done?

'She's done it. Ditto's won her third ticket. Now she's Champion Ditto. And look what I've bought her – a lovely blue and gold collar. Come on, Annika, let's go and see Ditto having her photos taken and Ditto in the champions' group.'

We applauded as Ditto strutted her stuff. Dearest, Darling, Damnable, Delectable, Delicious Ditto. I mustn't feel envious. But I do.

I did a very wicked thing. It gave me a guilty conscience – for about two minutes! I told Ditto that now she was a champion, she would have the letters CH in front of her name and that

Happiness is a Frisbee in the sunshine

would mean she would be sent to China. I know it was cruel but it was just a piece of fun. She looked very forlorn.

As we walked back to the car, our owner wearing Ditto's massive rosettes, a family stopped near us. Our owner was happily chatting to friends who were all singing the Damnable Ditto's praises, but the family were interested only in me.

'Look at that beautiful black-and-white corgi. Of course she's a champion. See the owner's rosettes. And look at that funny little spotty, blotchy mongrel walking by her side – half dachshund, half blue merle collie. It is so strange to see such funny little mongrels at shows. But probably someone would love her.

'But as for that gorgeous black-and-white corgi, well there's a real show winner. What a champion!'

The mother took hold of my smart red collar.

'Look, she's called Annika.'

Oh, how marvellous. They thought I was the champion with the rosettes. They thought Ditto was just my little silver sidekick. I chuckled to myself; eyes and teeth, eyes and teeth.

But Ditto was just happy that they thought I was the special one. She just glowed with pride at me.

'Oh, Annika. Thank you so much for letting me win today. Will you teach me to play football when we get home?'

'Yes, and I'll even help teach your puppies one day!'

'I was thinking about that. I really don't want to go to China. I met this lovely boy today – black and white and looks just like you. He wagged his tail and quivered his nose at me. I heard his owner talking to our owner and saying we could have some lovely puppies. He's so handsome.

That's champion, Ditto. Just champion!

'If I do have puppies, would you help me, dear Annika? Would you teach them to make their ears stand up and how to go up and down stairs, not to eat turkey or grapes and all those special skills that Cardigan corgis need? Would you help me with the puppies, Annika?

'But the thing is I wouldn't want to keep any of them. They would all have to go to lovely homes. We would see them occasionally at shows. Does that sound irresponsible? But I'm so happy with just you and Edward and Sophie and our owner. I don't want to share things with puppies. That would be horrid. They might pinch my toys and chews. I want it just to be us.'

'Yes, me too, Ditto. Let's go home and celebrate with a dip in the duck pond. Bet I can get muddier and smellier than you!'

'Bet you can't, Annika. Bet you can't!' Now I'm a champion I want to get so dirty that I never have to go to show again – ever!

Happiness is celebrating in the duck pond!